Mission Praise

Compiled by
Peter Horrobin and Greg Leavers

MUSICIANS' EDITION
VOLUME 1
1 – 261

Marshall Pickering

William Collins Sons & Co. Ltd.
London · Glasgow · Sydney · Auckland
Toronto · Johannesburg

First published in Great Britain in 1990 by Marshall Pickering

Marshall Pickering is an imprint of
Collins Religious Division,
part of the Collins Publishing Group
8 Grafton Street, London W1X 3LA

Music and text set by Barnes Music Engraving Ltd, East Sussex, England
Printed in Great Britain by Martins of Berwick

ISBN 0 551 02266 3

Music Edition   ISBN 0 551 01986 7

Words Edition   ISBN 0 551 01979 4 (Single copy)
                         ISBN 0 551 01977 8 (Pack of 25)

Large Print
  Words Edition   ISBN 0 551 01978 6

Musicians' Edition vol. 2 ISBN 0 551 02267 1
                   vol. 3 ISBN 0 551 02268 X
                         ISBN 0 551 02313 9 (Pack of three volumes)

Preface

This combined volume of Mission Praise brings together the original volume that was compiled for Mission England with the second and supplementary volumes. The contents of these three books, with the addition of some extra items, and now numbering 798 songs, has been structured so as to be a comprehensive hymn and song book for church and general use.

The success of Mission Praise owes much to its strategy of embracing the best of the old with the best of the new, freely mixing together both traditional hymns and modern songs. As such the volumes have gained wide acceptance with all ages and, indeed, a very wide range of church congregations.

The large and comprehensive subject and music indexes will be an invaluable aid to the selection of items for use throughout the church's year, at all special events in church and family life and for other special services.

The vision for the original Mission Praise volume eventually extended far beyond our initial expectations, and we give thanks to God for the way in which the collection opened up major new dimensions of praise and worship in many churches. Our prayer for this combined edition is that the blessings enjoyed by those who used the first volume of Mission Praise will be shared by all who use this combined volume.

Peter Horrobin and Greg Leavers

1   A new commandment

Words: from John 13
Music: Unknown
arranged Andy Silver

A new com-mand-ment I give un-to you, that you

love one an-oth-er as I have loved you, that you

love one an-oth-er as I have loved you. By

this shall all men know that you are My dis-ci-ples, if

you have love one for an - oth - er._____ By

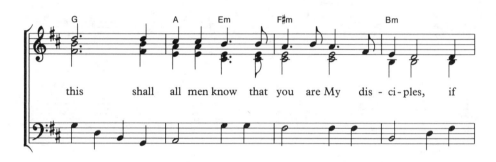

this shall all men know that you are My dis - ci - ples, if

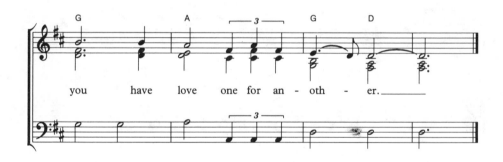

you have love one for an - oth - er._____

A new commandment I give unto you,
that you love one another as I have loved you,
that you love one another as I have loved you.

By this shall all men know that you are My disciples,
if you have love one for another.
By this shall all men know that you are My disciples,
if you have love one for another.

2

A safe stronghold

EIN' FESTE BURG   87 87 66 667

Words: Martin Luther (1483–1546)
tr. Thomas Carlyle (1795–1881)
Music: melody by Martin Luther (1483–1546)

A safe strong-hold our God is still, a trus-ty__ shield and__ wea - pon; He'll help us__ clear__ from all__ the ill that has us__ now o'er - tak - en. The an-cient prince of hell has__ risen with pur-pose fell; strong mail of craft and power he

wear-eth in— this— hour; on earth is— not his— fel - low.

1 A safe stronghold our God is still,
a trusty shield and weapon;
He'll help us clear from all the ill
that has us now o'ertaken.
The ancient prince of hell
has risen with purpose fell;
strong mail of craft and power
he weareth in this hour;
on earth is not his fellow.

2 With force of arms we nothing can,
full soon were we down-ridden;
but for us fights the proper Man
whom God Himself has bidden.
Ask ye: Who is this same?
Christ Jesus is His name,
the Lord Sabaoth's Son;
He, and no other one,
shall conquer in the battle.

3 And were this world all devils o'er,
and watching to devour us,
we lay it not to heart so sore;
not they can overpower us.
And let the prince of ill
look grim as e'er he will,
he harms us not a whit;
for why? his doom is writ;
a word shall quickly slay him.

4 God's word, for all their craft and force,
one moment will not linger,
but, spite of hell, shall have its course;
'tis written by His finger.
And though they take our life,
goods, honour, children, wife,
yet is their profit small;
these things shall vanish all,
the city of God remaineth.

3 Abba Father

Words and music: Dave Bilbrough
Music arranged Roland Fudge

4 Abide with me

EVENTIDE 10 10 10 10

Words: H F Lyte (1793–1847)
Music: W H Monk (1823–89)

A - bide with me; fast falls the e - ven - tide;

the___ dark - ness deep - ens; Lord, with me a - bide;

when__ o - ther help - ers___ fail, and com - forts flee,

help of the help - less, O a - bide with me.

1 Abide with me; fast falls the eventide;
   the darkness deepens; Lord, with me abide;
   when other helpers fail, and comforts flee,
   help of the helpless, O abide with me.

2 Swift to its close ebbs out life's little day;
   earth's joys grown dim, its glories pass away;
   change and decay in all around I see:
   O Thou who changest not, abide with me!

3 I need Thy presence every passing hour;
   what but Thy grace can foil the tempter's power?
   Who like Thyself my guide and stay can be?
   Through cloud and sunshine, O abide with me.

4 I fear no foe with Thee at hand to bless;
   ills have no weight, and tears no bitterness.
   Where is death's sting? where, grave, thy victory?
   I triumph still, if Thou abide with me.

5 Hold Thou Thy cross before my closing eyes,
   shine through the gloom, and point me to the skies;
   heaven's morning breaks, and earth's vain shadows flee:
   in life, in death, O Lord, abide with me!

5 Above the voices of the world

Words: Timothy Dudley-Smith
Music: Phil Burt

1 A - bove the voi - ces of the world a - round me,_____ my_
2 What can I of - fer Him who calls me to__ Him?_____ On -
3 Lord, I be - lieve; help now my un - be - liev - ing;_____ I_

hopes and dreams, my cares and loves and fears,_____ the_
- ly the wastes of sin and self and shame;_____ a__
come in faith be - cause Your pro - mise stands;_____ Your

long a - wait - ed call of Christ has found me,_____ the_
mind con-fused, a heart that ne - ver knew Him,_____ a__
word of par - don and of peace re - ceiv - ing,_____ all_

voice of Je - sus e - choes in my ears:_____
tongue un - skilled at nam - ing Je - sus' name._____
that I am__ I place with - in Your hands._____

6

Ah Lord God

Words and music: Kay Chance

7 All creatures of our God and King

LASST UNS ERFREUEN   88 44 88 with refrain

Words: St Francis of Assisi (1182–1226)
tr. William Henry Draper (1855–1933)
Music: melody from *Geistliche Kirchengessang*
Cologne, 1623
arranged R Vaughan Williams (1872–1958)

All crea-tures of our God and King, lift up your voice and with us sing: Hal - le - lu - jah, hal - le - lu - jah! Thou burn-ing sun with gold-en beam, thou sil-ver moon with soft-er gleam: O___ praise Him, O___ praise Him, Hal - le -

1 All creatures of our God and King,
  lift up your voice and with us sing:
  Hallelujah, hallelujah!
  Thou burning sun with golden beam,
  thou silver moon with softer gleam:
    O praise Him, O praise Him,
    Hallelujah, hallelujah, hallelujah!

2 Thou rushing wind that art so strong,
  ye clouds that sail in heaven along,
  O praise Him, hallelujah!
  Thou rising morn, in praise rejoice,
  ye lights of evening, find a voice:
    O praise Him . . .

3 Thou flowing water, pure and clear,
  make music for thy Lord to hear,
  Hallelujah, hallelujah!
  Thou fire so masterful and bright,
  that givest man both warmth and light:
    O praise Him . . .

4 And all ye men of tender heart,
  forgiving others, take your part,
  O sing ye, hallelujah!
  Ye who long pain and sorrow bear,
  praise God and on Him cast your care:
    O praise Him . . .

5 Let all things their Creator bless,
  and worship Him in humbleness,
  O praise Him, hallelujah!
  Praise, praise the Father, praise the Son,
  and praise the Spirit, Three-in-One:
    O praise Him . . .

8
All earth was dark

Words and music: J Daniels
and P Thompson
Music arranged Christopher Norton

migh - ty___ flame,   till   ev - ery heart,   con -
- sumed by love, shall_ rise   to___ praise Your ho - ly
name.

1 All earth was dark until You spoke,
    then all was light and all was peace.
    Yet still, oh God, so many wait,
    to see the flame of love released.
        Lights to the world, oh Light of man,
        kindle in us a mighty flame,
        till every heart, consumed by love,
        shall rise to praise Your holy name.

2 In Christ You gave Your gift of life
    to save us from the depth of night.
    Oh come and set our spirits free,
    and draw us to Your perfect light.
        Lights to the world, . . .

3 Where there is fear, may we bring joy,
    and healing to a world in pain.
    Lord, build Your kingdom through our lives,
    till Jesus walks this earth again.
        Lights to the world, . . .

4 O burn in us that we may burn
    with love that triumphs in despair.
    And touch our lives with such a fire,
    that souls may search and find You there.
        Lights to the world, . . .

9   All glory, laud and honour

ST THEODULPH   76 76 D

Words: Theodulph of Orleans (c750–821)
tr. J M Neale (1818–66)
Melody by Melchior Teschner (c1615)
Harmony from J S Bach (1685–1750)

All glo - ry, laud and hon - our to Thee, Re - deem - er,

King, to whom the lips of child - ren made

sweet ho - san - nas ring. Thou art__ the__ King of

Is - rael, Thou Da - vid's roy - al__ Son, who

in the Lord's name com - est, the King and bless - èd__ one.

1 All glory, laud and honour
   to Thee, Redeemer, King,
   to whom the lips of children
   made sweet hosannas ring.
   Thou art the King of Israel,
   Thou David's royal Son,
   who in the Lord's name comest,
   the King and blessèd one.

2 The company of angels
   are praising Thee on high,
   and mortal men and all things
   created make reply.
   The people of the Hebrews
   with psalms before Thee went;
   our praise and prayer and anthems
   before Thee we present.

3 To Thee before Thy passion
   they sang their hymns of praise;
   to Thee now high exalted
   our melody we raise.
   Thou didst accept their praises;
   accept the prayers we bring,
   who in all good delightest,
   Thou good and gracious King.

10 All around me, Lord

Words and music: Greg Leavers
Music arranged Phil Burt

A round in 3 parts

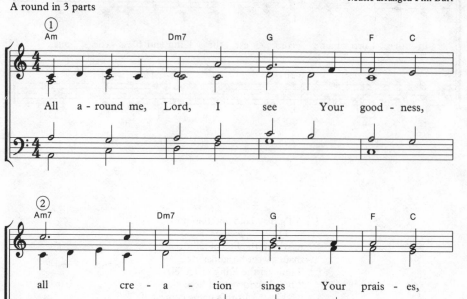

All around me, Lord, I see Your goodness,
all creation sings Your praises,
all the world cries, 'God is love!'

All hail King Jesus

Words and music: Unknown
Music arranged Roland Fudge

All hail the Lamb

Words and music: Dave Bilbrough

13(i) All hail the power of Jesus' name!

MILES LANE   CM

Words: Edward Perronet (1726–92)
and John Rippon (1751–1836)
Music: W Shrubsole (1760–1806)

All hail the power of Je - sus' name! let an - gels_ pros-trate fall; bring forth the roy - al di - a - dem, and crown Him, crown Him, crown_ Him, crown Him Lord of all.

1 All hail the power of Jesus' name!
   let angels prostrate fall;
   bring forth the royal diadem,
   and crown Him Lord of all.

2 Crown Him, ye martyrs of our God,
   who from His altar call;
   extol the stem of Jesse's rod,
   and crown Him Lord of all.

3 Ye seed of Israel's chosen race,
   and ransomed from the fall,
   hail Him who saves you by His grace,
   and crown Him Lord of all.

4 Let every kindred, every tribe,
   on this terrestrial ball,
   to Him all majesty ascribe,
   and crown Him Lord of all.

5 O that with yonder sacred throng
   we at His feet may fall,
   join in the everlasting song,
   and crown Him Lord of all!

13(ii) All hail the power of Jesus' name!

DIADEM 86 86 extended

Music: James Ellor (1819–99)

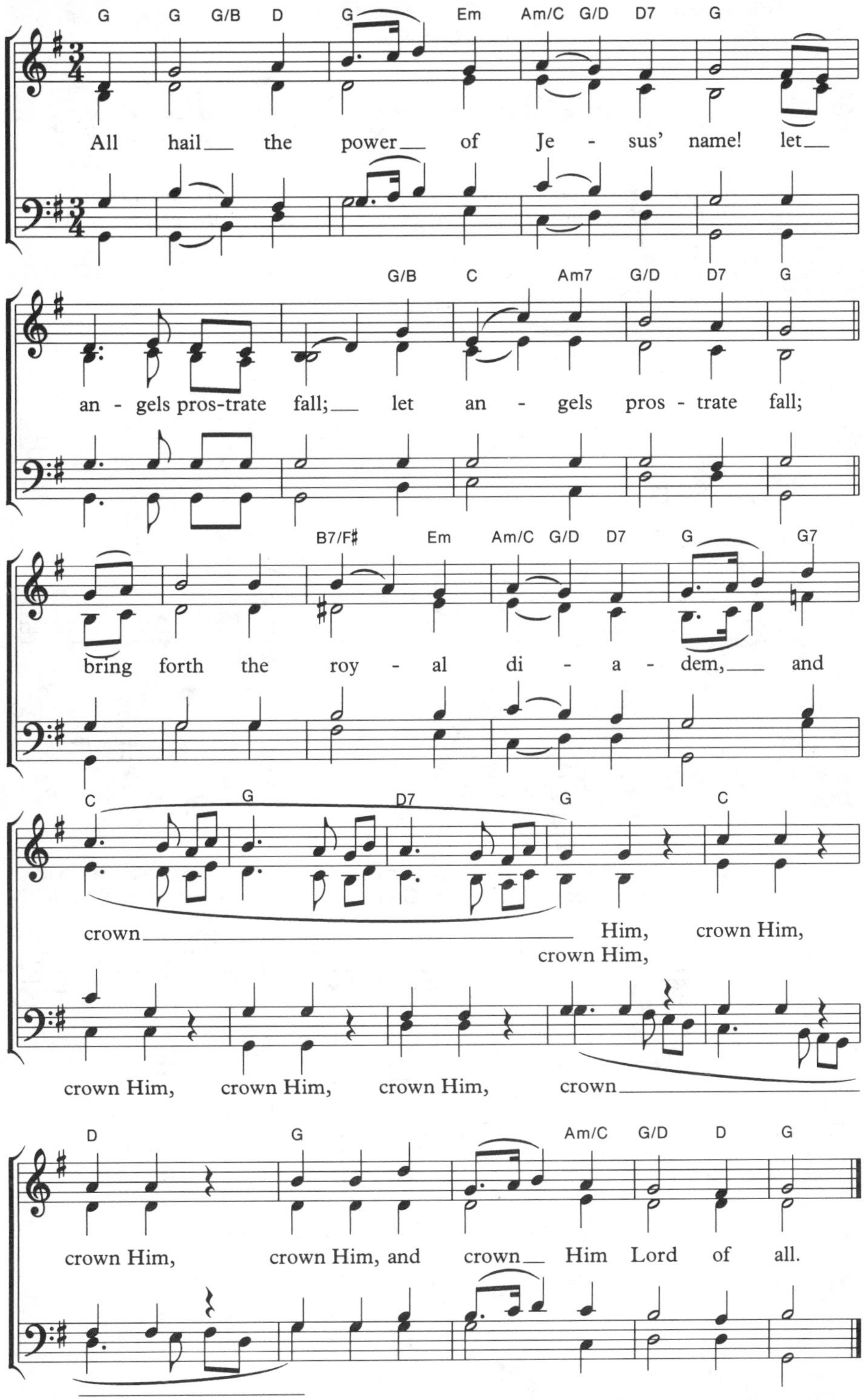

G G G/B D G Em Am/C G/D D7 G
All hail__ the power__ of Je - sus' name! let__
G/B C Am7 G/D D7 G
an - gels pros-trate fall;__ let an - gels pros - trate fall;
B7/F# Em Am/C G/D D7 G G7
bring forth the roy - al di - a - dem,__ and
C G D7 G C
crown__ Him, crown Him,
crown Him,
crown Him, crown Him, crown Him, crown__
D G Am/C G/D D G
crown Him, crown Him, and crown__ Him Lord of all.

14   All heaven declares

Words: Tricia Richards
Music: Noel Richards

With majesty

Capo 1(A)

1 All heaven de-clares the glo-ry of the ris - en Lord; who can com-pare with the beau-ty of the Lord? For ev-er He will be the Lamb up-on_ the throne;

2 I will pro-claim the glo-ry of the ris - en Lord, who once was slain to re-con-cile_ man to God. For ev-er You will be the Lamb up-on_ the throne;

I glad-ly bow the knee,   and wor-ship Him a-lone.
I glad-ly bow the knee,   and wor-ship You a-lone.

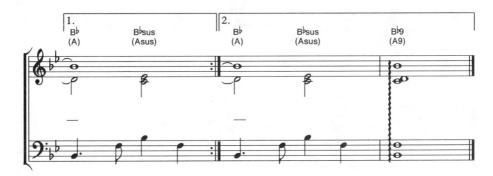

1   All heaven declares
    the glory of the risen Lord;
    who can compare
    with the beauty of the Lord?
    For ever He will be
    the Lamb upon the throne;
    I gladly bow the knee,
    and worship Him alone.

2   I will proclaim
    the glory of the risen Lord,
    who once was slain
    to reconcile man to God.
    For ever You will be
    the Lamb upon the throne;
    I gladly bow the knee,
    and worship You alone.

15 All heaven waits

Words and music: Graham Kendrick
and Chris Rolinson
Music arranged Christopher Norton

All hea-ven waits with ba-ted breath, for saints on earth to pray; ma-jes-tic an-gels rea-dy stand with swords of fie-ry blade. As-tound-ing power a - waits a word from God's re-splen-dent throne;_____ but God a-waits our prayer of faith that

cries,   'Your   will   be   done.'

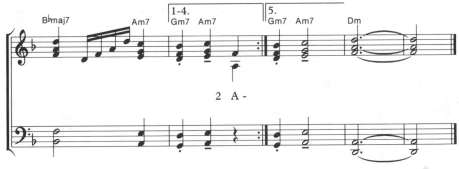

2 A -

1 All heaven waits with bated breath,
   for saints on earth to pray;
   majestic angels ready stand
   with swords of fiery blade.
   Astounding power awaits a word
   from God's resplendent throne;
   but God awaits our prayer of faith
   that cries, 'Your will be done.'

2 Awake, O Church, arise and pray,
   complaining words discard;
   the Spirit comes to fill your mouth
   with truth, His mighty sword.
   Go place your feet on Satan's ground,
   and there proclaim Christ's name;
   in step with heaven's armies march
   to conquer and to reign!

WOMEN
3 Now in our hearts and on our lips
   the word of faith is near;
   let heaven's will on earth be done,
   let heaven flow from here.
MEN
   Come blend your prayers with Jesus' own,
   before the Father's throne;
   and as the incense clouds ascend,
   God's holy fire rains down.

4 Soon comes the day when, with a shout,
   King Jesus shall appear;
   and with Him all the Church
   from every age shall fill the air.
   The brightness of His coming shall
   consume the lawless one;
   as with a word the breath of God
   tears down his rebel throne.

5 One body here by heaven inspired,
   we seek prophetic power;
   in Christ agreed one heart and voice
   to speak this day, this hour.
   In every place where chaos rules,
   and evil forces brood,
   let Jesus' voice speak like the roar
   of a great multitude.

16 All my hope on God is founded

MICHAEL   87 87 33 7

Words: after J Neander (1650–80)
Robert Bridges (1844–1930)
Music: Herbert Howells (1892–1983)

All my hope on God is_ found - ed, all my trust He shall_ re - new; He, my guide through chang-ing or - der, on - ly good and on - ly true. God un - known, He a - -lone calls my heart to be_ His own.

1   All my hope on God is founded,
    all my trust He shall renew;
    He, my guide through changing order,
    only good and only true.
      God unknown,
      He alone
    calls my heart to be His own.

2   Pride of man and earthly glory,
    sword and crown betray His trust;
    all that human toil can fashion,
    tower and temple, fall to dust.
      But God's power,
      hour by hour,
    is my temple and my tower.

3   Day by day our mighty giver
    grants to us His gifts of love;
    in His will our souls find pleasure,
    leading to our home above.
      Love shall stand
      at His hand,
    joy shall wait for His command.

4   Still from man to God eternal
    sacrifice of praise be done,
    high above all praises praising
    for the gift of Christ His Son.
      Hear Christ's call
      one and all:
    we who follow shall not fall.

17   All my life, Lord

Words and music: Andy and Becky Silver

For two groups of singers

All my life, Lord,___ to You I want to give;___ this is my wor - ship,___ please show me how to live.___ Take ev-ery part of me,___ make it Your own, me on the cross, Lord,___ You on the throne.

18 All over the world

Words and music: Roy Turner
Music arranged Roland Fudge

All o-ver the world the Spi-rit is mov-ing,
All o-ver His church God's Spi-rit is mov-ing,
Right here in this place the Spi-rit is mov-ing,

all o-ver the world as the pro-phet said it would be;
all o-ver His church as the pro-phet said it would be;
right here in this place as the pro-phet said it would be;

all o-ver the world there's a migh-ty re-ve-la-tion of the
all o-ver His church there's a migh-ty re-ve-la-tion of the
right here in this place there's a migh-ty re-ve-la-tion of the

glo-ry of the Lord, as the wa-ters co-ver the sea.
glo-ry of the Lord, as the wa-ters co-ver the sea.
glo-ry of the Lord, as the wa-ters co-ver the sea.

19 All praise to our redeeming Lord

LUCIUS CM

Words: Charles Wesley (1707–88)
Music: attributed to *Templi Carmina*, 1829

1 All praise to our redeeming Lord,
who joins us by His grace,
and bids us each to each restored,
together seek His face.

2 He bids us build each other up;
and, gathered into one,
to our high calling's glorious hope
we hand in hand go on.

3 The gift which He on one bestows,
we all delight to prove;
the grace through every vessel flows,
in purest streams of love.

4 Ev'n now we think and speak the same,
and cordially agree;
concentrated all, through Jesu's name,
in perfect harmony.

5 We all partake the joy of one,
the common peace we feel,
a peace to sensual minds unknown,
a joy unspeakable.

6 And if our fellowship below
in Jesus be so sweet,
what heights of rapture shall we know
when round His throne we meet!

20 All people that on earth do dwell

OLD HUNDREDTH LM

Words: William Kethe (1520–94)
Music: Melody from the *Genevan Psalter*, 1551

1 All people that on earth do dwell,
   Sing to the Lord with cheerful voice;
   Him serve with mirth, His praise forth tell;
   come ye before Him and rejoice.

2 The Lord, ye know, is God indeed:
   without our aid He did us make:
   we are His folk, He doth us feed;
   and for His sheep He doth us take.

3 O enter then His gates with praise,
   approach with joy His courts unto;
   praise, laud, and bless His name always,
   for it is seemly so to do.

4 For why? The Lord our God is good;
   His mercy is for ever sure;
   His truth at all times firmly stood,
   and shall from age to age endure.

21 All the riches of His grace

Words and music: Jan Harrington

With simplicity, flowing

All the rich - es of His grace, all the ful - ness of His bless-ings, all the sweet - ness of His love_____ He gives to you,_____ He gives to me. All the me.

1 Oh, the blood of_ Je - sus, oh, the blood of_ Je - sus,
2 Oh, the word of_ Je - sus, oh, the word of_ Je - sus,
3 Oh, the love of_ Je - sus, oh, the love of_ Je - sus,

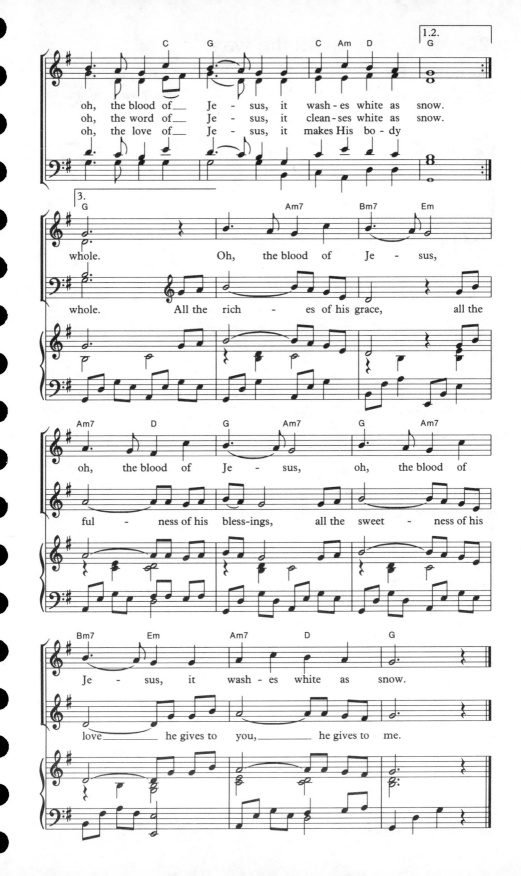

22 All the way

ALL THE WAY   87 87 D

Words: Frances van Alstyne (1820–1915)
(Fanny J Crosby)
Music: Robert Lowry (1826–99)
arranged Phil Burt

All the way my Sav-iour leads me; what have I to ask be -side? Can I doubt His ten-der mer - cy, who through life has been my guide? Heaven-ly peace, di - vin - est com - fort, here by faith in Him to dwell! For I

know   what-e'er be - fall   me,   Je - sus   do - eth   all   things   well.

1 All the way my Saviour leads me;
   what have I to ask beside?
   Can I doubt His tender mercy,
   who through life has been my guide?
   Heavenly peace, divinest comfort,
   here by faith in Him to dwell!
   For I know whate'er befall me,
   Jesus doeth all things well.

2 All the way my Saviour leads me,
   cheers each winding path I tread,
   gives me grace for every trial,
   feeds me with the living bread.
   Though my weary steps may falter,
   and my soul a-thirst may be,
   gushing from the rock before me,
   Lo! a spring of joy I see.

3 All the way my Saviour leads me,
   O the fulness of His love!
   Perfect rest to me is promised
   in my Father's house above.
   When my spirit, clothed, immortal,
   wings its flight to realms of day,
   this, my song through endless ages:
   Jesus led me all the way!

23(i) All things bright and beautiful

ALL THINGS BRIGHT AND BEAUTIFUL   76 76 with refrain

Words: Cecil F Alexander (1818–95)
Music: W H Monk (1823–89)

All things bright and beau-ti-ful, all_ crea-tures great and small,_

all things wise and won-der-ful, the_ Lord God_ made them all. *Fine*

Each lit-tle flower that o - pens, each lit-tle bird that sings,___ He

made their glow-ing co - lours, He made their ti - ny wings. *D.C.*

All things bright and beautiful,
all creatures great and small,
all things wise and wonderful,
the Lord God made them all.

1 Each little flower that opens,
  each little bird that sings,
  He made their glowing colours,
  He made their tiny wings.
      All things bright . . .

2 The purple-headed mountain,
  the river running by,
  the sunset, and the morning
  that brightens up the sky;
      All things bright . . .

3 The cold wind in the winter,
  the pleasant summer sun,
  the ripe fruits in the garden,
  He made them every one.
      All things bright . . .

4 He gave us eyes to see them,
  and lips that we might tell
  how great is God almighty,
  who has made all things well.
      All things bright . . .

23(ii)   All things bright and beautiful

Royal Oak   76 76 with refrain

Words: Cecil F Alexander (1818–95)
Music: Traditional English melody
arranged Martin Shaw (1875–1958)

All things bright and beau-ti-ful, all crea-tures great and small,

all things wise and won-der-ful, the Lord God made them all. *Fine*

Each lit-tle flower that o-pens, each lit-tle bird that sings, He_

made their glow-ing_ col-ours, He_ made their ti-ny_ wings. *D.C.*

All things bright and beautiful,
all creatures great and small,
all things wise and wonderful,
the Lord God made them all.

1 Each little flower that opens,
   each little bird that sings,
   He made their glowing colours,
   He made their tiny wings.
   All things bright . . .

2 The purple-headed mountain,
   the river running by,
   the sunset, and the morning
   that brightens up the sky;
   All things bright . . .

3 The cold wind in the winter,
   the pleasant summer sun,
   the ripe fruits in the garden,
   He made them every one.
   All things bright . . .

4 He gave us eyes to see them,
   and lips that we might tell
   how great is God almighty,
   who has made all things well.
   All things bright . . .

24   All things praise Thee

TE LAUDANT OMNIA   77 77 77

Words: G W Conder (1821–74)
Music: J F Swift (1847–1931)

All things praise Thee, Lord most high, heaven and earth and sea and sky,
all were for Thy glo-ry made, that Thy great-ness, thus dis-played,
should all wor-ship bring to Thee; all things praise Thee: Lord, may we.

1   All things praise Thee, Lord most high,
heaven and earth and sea and sky,
all were for Thy glory made,
that Thy greatness, thus displayed,
should all worship bring to Thee;
all things praise Thee: Lord, may we.

2   All things praise Thee: night to night
sings in silent hymns of light;
all things praise Thee: day to day
chants Thy power in burning ray;
time and space are praising Thee;
all things praise Thee: Lord, may we.

3   All things praise Thee, high and low,
rain and dew, and seven-hued bow,
crimson sunset, fleecy cloud,
rippling stream, and tempest loud,
summer, winter – all to Thee
glory render: Lord, may we.

4   All things praise Thee, heaven's high
    shrine
rings with melody divine;
lowly bending at Thy feet,
seraph and archangel meet;
this their highest bliss, to be
ever praising: Lord, may we.

5   All things praise Thee, gracious Lord,
great Creator, powerful Word,
omnipresent Spirit, now
at Thy feet we humbly bow,
lift our hearts in praise to Thee;
all things praise Thee: Lord, may we.

25 All to Jesus I surrender

Words: J W Van De Venter
Music: W S Weedon
arranged Roland Fudge

1 All to Je-sus I sur-ren-der, all to Him I free-ly give;
2 All to Je-sus I sur-ren-der, hum-bly at His feet I bow;
3 All to Je-sus I sur-ren-der, make me, Sav-iour, whol-ly Thine;
4 All to Je-sus I sur-ren-der, Lord, I give my-self to Thee;
5 All to Je-sus I sur-ren-der, now I feel the sac-red flame;

I will ev-er love and trust Him, in His pres-ence dai-ly live.
world-ly plea-sures all for-sa-ken, take me, Je-sus, take me now.
let me feel the Ho-ly Spi-rit, tru-ly know that Thou art mine.
fill me with Thy love and pow-er, let Thy bless-ing fall on me.
oh, the joy of full sal-va-tion! Glo-ry, glo-ry to His name!

I sur-ren-der all,___ I sur-ren-der all,___

all to Thee, my bless-ed Sav-iour, I sur-ren-der all.

26 All you that pass by

WAREHAM   55 11 D

Words: Charles Wesley (1707–88) altd.
Music: W Knapp (1698–1768)

All you that pass by, to Je-sus draw nigh;

to you is it no-thing that Je-sus should die?

Your ran-som and and peace, your sure-ty He is,

come, see if there ev-er was sor-row like His.

1 All you that pass by,
   to Jesus draw nigh;
   to you is it nothing that Jesus should die?
   Your ransom and peace,
   your surety He is,
   come, see if there ever was sorrow like His.

2 He dies to atone
   for sins not His own.
   Your debt He has paid and your work He has done:
   you all may receive
   the peace He did leave,
   who made intercession, 'My Father, forgive.'

3 For you and for me
   He prayed on the tree:
   the prayer is accepted, the sinner is free.
   The sinner am I,
   who on Jesus rely,
   and come for the pardon God cannot deny.

4 His death is my plea;
   my advocate see,
   and hear the blood speak that has answered for me:
   He purchased the grace
   which now I embrace;
   O Father, You know Jesus died in my place!

Almighty God

Words and music: Austin Martin
Music arranged Roland Fudge

Worshipfully

Al-migh-ty God, we bring You praise
for Your Son, the Word of God;
by whose power the world was made,
by whose blood we are re-deemed.

Morn-ing Star,_____ the Fa-ther's glo - ry,_____

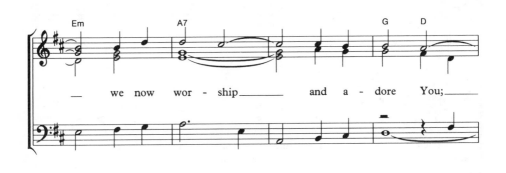

_ we now wor - ship_____ and a - dore You;_____

_ in our hearts_____ Your light has ris - en;_____

_ Je - sus, Lord,_____ we wor - ship You.

28 Almighty God, our heavenly Father

Words: from *The Alternative Service Book 1980*
Music: Chris Rolinson

With feeling

Al-migh-ty God, our hea-ven-ly Fa-ther, we have sinned a-gainst___ You and a-gainst our fel-low men,___ in thought and word and deed, through neg-li-gence,___ through weak-ness, through our

Alleluia

Words and music: Anon
Music arranged Betty Pulkingham

With quiet adoration

Al - le - lu - ia,_____ Al - le - lu - ia,_____ Al - le -

- lu - ia,_____ Al - le - lu - ia,_____ Al - le - lu - ia._____

1 Alleluia (*8 times*)

2 How I love Him

3 Blessed Jesus

4 My Redeemer

5 Jesus is Lord

6 Alleluia

30   Alleluia, alleluia, give thanks

ALLELUIA No. 1

Words and music: Donald Fishel
Music arranged Betty Pulkingham

Capo 3(D)

Al-le - lu - ia, al-le - lu - ia, give thanks to the ris-en Lord; al-le -

last time only

- lu - ia, al-le - lu - ia, give praise to His name.   name.

Je - sus is Lord of all the＿ earth,

He is the King of cre - a - tion.   Al-le -

Alleluia, alleluia,
give thanks to the risen Lord;
alleluia, alleluia,
give praise to His name.

1   Jesus is Lord of all the earth,
    He is the King of creation.
      Alleluia, alleluia . . .

2   Spread the good news o'er all the earth,
    Jesus has died and has risen.
      Alleluia, alleluia . . .

3   We have been crucified with Christ;
    now we shall live for ever.
      Alleluia, alleluia . . .

4   God has proclaimed the just reward,
    life for all men, alleluia.
      Alleluia, alleluia . . .

5   Come let us praise the living God,
    joyfully sing to our Saviour:
      Alleluia, alleluia . . .

31 Amazing grace

AMAZING GRACE   CM

Words: John Newton (1725–1807)
Music: Traditional
arranged Roland Fudge

1   Amazing grace – how sweet the sound –
    that saved a wretch like me!
    I once was lost, but now am found,
    was blind, but now I see.

2   'Twas grace that taught my heart to fear,
    and grace my fears relieved;
    how precious did that grace appear
    the hour I first believed.

3   Through many dangers, toils and snares,
    I have already come;
    'tis grace hath brought me safe thus far,
    and grace will lead me home.

4   When we've been there ten thousand years
    bright shining as the sun,
    we've no less days to sing God's praise
    than when we've first begun.

32 An army of ordinary people

Words and music: Dave Bilbrough
Music arranged Roland Fudge

With feeling

An ar-my of or-di-na-ry peo-ple,___ a king-dom where love is the key,___ a ci-ty, a light to the na-tions,___ heirs to the pro-mise are we.___ A peo-ple_ whose life is in Je-sus,___ a na-tion to-ge-ther we

but the time has now come,   *when the child-ren of*

pro-mise   *shall flow to-ge-ther as*   *one.*

1   An army of ordinary people,
    a kingdom where love is the key,
    a city, a light to the nations,
    heirs to the promise are we.
    A people whose life is in Jesus,
    a nation together we stand;
    only through grace are we worthy,
    inheritors of the land.
      A new day is dawning,
      a new age to come,
      when the children of promise
      shall flow together as one:
      a truth long neglected,
      but the time has now come,
      when the children of promise
      shall flow together as one.

2   A people without recognition,
    but with Him a destiny sealed,
    called to a heavenly vision:
    His purpose shall be fulfilled.
    Come let us stand strong together,
    abandon ourselves to the King;
    His love shall be ours for ever,
    this victory song we shall sing.
      A new day . . .

33 And can it be

SAGINA   88 88 88

Words: Charles Wesley (1707–88)
Music: Thomas Campbell (1825–76)

And can it be that I should gain an in-terest in the Sav-iour's blood? Died He for me, who caused His pain? For me, who Him to death pur-sued? A-maz-ing love! how can it be that Thou, my God, shouldst die for

me! A - maz - ing love! how can it

be that Thou, my God, shouldst die for me!

1 And can it be that I should gain
an interest in the Saviour's blood?
Died He for me, who caused His pain?
For me, who Him to death pursued?
Amazing love! how can it be
that Thou, my God, shouldst die for me!

2 'Tis mystery all! The Immortal dies:
who can explore His strange design?
In vain the first-born seraph tries
to sound the depths of love divine.
'Tis mercy all! let earth adore,
let angel minds inquire no more.

3 He left His Father's throne above –
so free, so infinite His grace –
emptied Himself of all but love,
and bled for Adam's helpless race.
'Tis mercy all, immense and free;
for, O my God, it found out me!

4 Long my imprisoned spirit lay
fast bound in sin and nature's night;
Thine eye diffused a quickening ray –
I woke, the dungeon flamed with light;
my chains fell off, my heart was free.
I rose, went forth, and followed Thee.

5 No condemnation now I dread;
Jesus, and all in Him, is mine!
Alive in Him, my living Head,
and clothed in righteousness divine,
bold I approach the eternal throne,
and claim the crown, through Christ, my own.

34 Angel voices ever singing

ANGEL VOICES   85 85 843

Words: Francis Pott (1832–1909)
Music: Edwin George Monk (1819–1900)

An - gel voi - ces ev - er sing - ing round Thy throne of light, an - gel harps for ev - er ring - ing, rest not day nor night; thou - sands on - ly live to bless Thee, and con - fess Thee Lord of might.

1   Angel voices ever singing
    round Thy throne of light,
    angel harps for ever ringing,
    rest not day nor night;
    thousands only live to bless Thee,
    and confess Thee Lord of might.

2   Thou who art beyond the farthest
    mortal eye can scan,
    can it be that Thou regardest
    songs of sinful man?
    Can we know that Thou art near us
    and wilt hear us? Yes, we can.

3   Yes, we know that Thou rejoicest
    o'er each work of Thine;
    Thou didst ears and hands and voices
    for Thy praise design;
    craftsman's art and music's measure
    for Thy pleasure all combine.

4   In Thy house, great God, we offer
    of Thine own to Thee;
    and for Thine acceptance proffer,
    all unworthily,
    hearts and minds and hands and voices
    in our choicest psalmody.

5   Honour, glory, might, and merit
    Thine shall ever be:
    Father, Son, and Holy Spirit,
    Blessèd Trinity:
    of the best that Thou hast given,
    earth and heaven render Thee.

35   Angels from the realms of glory

IRIS   87 87 with refrain

Words: J Montgomery (1771–1854)
in this version Jubilate Hymns
Music: French carol melody

An-gels from the_ realms of glo-ry, wing your flight through all the earth;

her-alds of cre - a-tion's sto-ry now pro-claim Mes - si-ah's birth!

Come_____ and_

wor - ship Christ, the new - born King;____

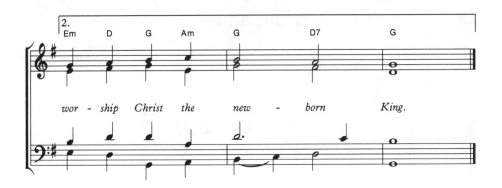

wor - ship Christ the new - born King.

1 Angels from the realms of glory,
  wing your flight through all the earth;
  heralds of creation's story
  now proclaim Messiah's birth!
    Come and worship
    Christ, the new-born King;
    come and worship,
    worship Christ the new-born King.

2 Shepherds in the fields abiding,
  watching by your flocks at night,
  God with man is now residing:
  see, there shines the infant light!
    Come and worship . . .

3 Wise men, leave your contemplations!
  brighter visions shine afar;
  seek in Him the hope of nations,
  you have seen His rising star:
    Come and worship . . .

4 Though an infant now we view Him,
  He will share His Father's throne,
  gather all the nations to Him;
  every knee shall then bow down:
    Come and worship . . .

36 Arise, shine

Words and music: Eric Glass
Music arranged Mimi Farra

37 As the deer

Words and music: Martin Nystrom

As the deer pants for the wa-ter, so my soul longs af - ter You. You a - lone are my heart's de - sire___ and I long to wor - ship You. *You a - lone are my strength, my shield, to You a - lone may my spi - rit yield.*

D	A/C♯	Bm	G	Em7	A7	D
(C)	(G/B)	(Am)	(F)	(Dm7)	(G7)	(C)

You a-lone are my heart's de-sire and I long to wor-ship You.

1 As the deer pants for the water,
   so my soul longs after You.
   You alone are my heart's desire
   and I long to worship You.
   You alone are my strength, my shield,
   to You alone may my spirit yield.
   You alone are my heart's desire
   and I long to worship You.

2 I want You more than gold or silver,
   only You can satisfy.
   You alone are the real joy-giver
   and the apple of my eye.
   You alone are . . .

3 You're my Friend and You're my Brother,
   even though You are a king.
   I love You more than any other,
   so much more than anything.
   You alone are . . .

38 As we are gathered

Words and music: John Daniels
Music arranged Roland Fudge

As we are gath - ered, Je - sus is here, one with each o - ther, Je - sus is here; joined by the Spi - rit, washed in His Blood,

39 As with gladness

Dix   77 77 77

Words: W C Dix (1837–98)
altered Horrobin/Leavers
Music: from a chorale by C Kocher (1786–72)

As with glad-ness men of old   did the guid-ing   star be-hold;

as with joy they hailed its light,   lead-ing on-ward, beam-ing bright,

so, most gra-cious God, may we   led by You for   ev-er   be.

1 As with gladness men of old
   did the guiding star behold;
   as with joy they hailed its light,
   leading onward, beaming bright,
   so, most gracious God, may we
   led by You for ever be.

2 As with joyful steps they sped,
   Saviour, to Your lowly bed,
   there to bend the knee before
   You whom heaven and earth adore,
   so may we with one accord,
   seek forgivness from our Lord.

3 As they offered gifts most rare,
   gold and frankincense and myrrh,
   so may we, cleansed from our sin,
   lives of service now begin,
   as in love our treasures bring,
   Christ, to You our heavenly King.

4 Holy Jesus, every day
   keep us in the narrow way;
   and when earthly things are past,
   bring our ransomed souls at last
   where they need no star to guide,
   where no clouds Your glory hide.

5 In the heavenly country bright
   need they no created light;
   You its light, its joy, its crown,
   You its sun which goes not down.
   There for ever may we sing
   Hallelujahs to our King.

40 Ascribe greatness

Words and music: Unknown
Music arranged Roland Fudge

Richly

As - cribe great-ness to our God the rock,___

His work is per-fect and all His ways are just.___

A God of faith - ful - ness___ and

with-out___ in - just - ice;___ good and up - right is He.___

up - right is He.___

41(i)   At the name of Jesus

EVELYNS   65 65 D

Words: Caroline Noel (1817–77)
Music: W H Monk (1823–89)

At the name of Je - sus___ ev - ery knee shall bow,

ev - ery tongue con - fess___ Him___ King of glo - ry___ now.___

'Tis the Fa-ther's plea - sure___ we___ should call Him Lord,___

who from the be - gin - ning___ was the migh - ty Word.

1 At the name of Jesus
   every knee shall bow,
   every tongue confess Him
   King of glory now.
   'Tis the Father's pleasure
   we should call Him Lord,
   who from the beginning
   was the mighty Word.

2 Mighty and mysterious
   in the highest height,
   God from everlasting,
   very Light of light.
   In the Father's bosom,
   with the Spirits blest,
   love, in love eternal,
   rest, in perfect rest.

optional.

3 Humbled for a season,
   to receive a name
   from the lips of sinners
   unto whom He came;
   faithfully He bore it
   spotless to the last,
   brought it back victorious,
   when from death He passed.

4 Bore it up triumphant
   with its human light,
   through all ranks of creatures,
   to the central height;
   to the throne of Godhead,
   to the Father's breast,
   filled it with the glory
   of that perfect rest.

5 In your hearts enthrone Him;
   there let Him subdue
   all that is not holy,
   all that is not true;
   crown Him as your captain
   in temptation's hour,
   let His will enfold you
   in its light and power.

6 Brothers, this Lord Jesus
   shall return again,
   with His Father's glory,
   with His angel-train;
   for all wreaths of empire
   meet upon His brow,
   and our hearts confess Him
   King of glory now.

41(ii)   At the name of Jesus

CAMBERWELL   65 65 D

Words: C M Noel (1817–77)
Music: Michael Brierley

At the name of Je - sus ev - ery knee shall bow, ev - ery tongue con - fess Him King of glo - ry now. 'Tis the Fa - ther's plea - sure we should call Him Lord,

Music: © 1960 Josef Weinberger Ltd,
12–14 Mortimer Street, London W1N 7RD

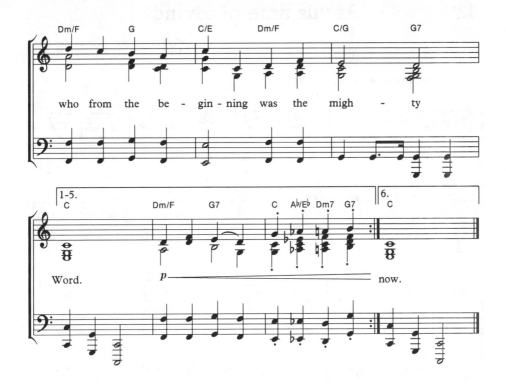

who from the be - gin - ning was the migh - ty

Word. *p* now.

1 At the name of Jesus
  every knee shall bow,
  every tongue confess Him
  King of glory now.
  'Tis the Father's pleasure
  we should call Him Lord,
  who from the beginning
  was the mighty Word.

2 Mighty and mysterious
  in the highest height,
  God from everlasting,
  very Light of light.
  In the Father's bosom,
  with the Spirits blest,
  love, in love eternal,
  rest, in perfect rest.

3 Humbled for a season,
  to receive a name
  from the lips of sinners
  unto whom He came;
  faithfully He bore it
  spotless to the last,
  brought it back victorious,
  when from death He passed.

4 Bore it up triumphant
  with its human light,
  through all ranks of creatures,
  to the central height;
  to the throne of Godhead,
  to the Father's breast,
  filled it with the glory
  of that perfect rest.

5 In your hearts enthrone Him;
  there let Him subdue
  all that is not holy,
  all that is not true;
  crown Him as your captain
  in temptation's hour,
  let His will enfold you
  in its light and power.

6 Brothers, this Lord Jesus
  shall return again,
  with His Father's glory,
  with His angel-train;
  for all wreaths of empire
  meet upon His brow,
  and our hearts confess Him
  King of glory now.

42   At this time of giving

Words and music: Graham Kendrick
Music arranged Christopher Norton

At this time of giving, glad-ly now we bring gifts of good-ness and mer-cy from a heaven-ly King. Earth could not con-tain the trea-sures hea-ven holds for you,

per - fect   joy   and   last - ing   plea-sures,   love   so   strong   and___

true.   lai.

At this time of giving,
gladly now we bring
gifts of goodness and mercy
from a heavenly King.

1 Earth could not contain the treasures
   heaven holds for you,
   perfect joy and lasting pleasures,
   love so strong and true.
       At this time of giving . . .

2 May His tender love surround you
   at this Christmastime;
   may you see His smiling face
   that in the darkness shines.
       At this time of giving . . .

3 But the many gifts He gives
   are all poured out from one;
   come receive the greatest gift,
   the gift of God's own Son.
       At this time of giving . . .

Last two choruses and verses:
Lai, lai, lai . . . *(etc.)*

43   At even, ere the sun was set

ANGELUS   LM

Words: Henry Twells (1823–1900)
Music: Melody by Georg Joseph
in Scheffler's *Heilige Seelenlust*, 1657

1 At even, ere the sun was set,
the sick, O Lord, around Thee lay;
O in what divers pains they met!
O with what joy they went away!

2 Once more 'tis eventide, and we,
oppressed with various ills, draw near;
what if Thy form we cannot see?
we know and feel that Thou art here.

3 O Saviour Christ, our woes dispel:
for some are sick, and some are sad,
and some have never loved Thee well,
and some have lost the love they had;

4 And some have found the world is vain,
yet from the world they break not free;
and some have friends who give them pain,
yet have not sought a friend in Thee;

5 And none, O Lord, have perfect rest,
for none are wholly free from sin;
and they who fain would serve Thee best
are conscious most of wrong within.

6 O Saviour Christ, Thou too art man;
Thou hast been troubled, tempted, tried;
Thy kind but searching glance can scan
the very wounds that shame would hide.

7 Thy touch has still its ancient power,
no word from Thee can fruitless fall;
hear, in this solemn evening hour,
and in Thy mercy heal us all.

44 At Your feet, O Lord

Words and music: Janis Miller

Unhurried

At Your feet, O Lord, we wait for You,

yearn-ing Lord, hun-gry Lord, for more of You.

Bowed be-fore You, Lord, we de-sire on-ly You:

fill us Lord, re-vive us Lord, with more of You.

45 At Your feet we fall

Words and music: Dave Fellingham
Music arranged David Peacock

With steady strength

At Your feet we fall, mighty ris-en Lord, as we come be-fore Your throne to wor-ship You. By Your Spi-rit's power You now draw our hearts, and we hear Your voice in tri-umph ring-ing clear:

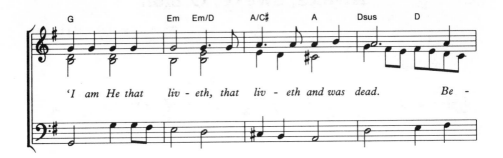

'I am He that liv - eth, that liv - eth and was dead. Be -

- hold, I am a - live for ev - er - more.

1   At Your feet we fall, mighty risen Lord,
    as we come before Your throne to worship You.
    By Your Spirit's power You now draw our hearts,
    and we hear Your voice in triumph ringing clear:
      'I am He that liveth,
      that liveth and was dead.
      Behold, I am alive
      for evermore.

2   There we see You stand, mighty risen Lord,
    clothed in garments pure and holy, shining bright;
    eyes of flashing fire, feet like burnished bronze,
    and the sound of many waters is Your voice.
      'I am He that liveth . . .

3   Like the shining sun in its noon-day strength,
    we now see the glory of Your wondrous face:
    once that face was marred, but now You're glorified;
    and Your words, like a two-edged sword have mighty power.
      'I am He that liveth . . .

46 Awake, awake, O Zion

Words and music: David J Hadden

Triumphantly

A - wake, a - wake, O Zi - on, come

clothe your - self with strength._____ A -

Put on your gar - ments of splen -

- dour, O Je - ru - sa - lem;_____

Words and music: © 1981 Springtide/Word Music (UK), (a division of Word (UK) Ltd)
9 Holdom Avenue, Bletchley, Milton Keynes MK1 1QR, UK

come sing your songs of joy and tri - umph, see that

D.C. al Coda   ⊕ CODA

your God reigns._____   A -

Awake, awake, O Zion,
come clothe yourself with strength.
Awake, awake, O Zion,
come clothe yourself with strength.

1 Put on your garments of splendour,
    O Jerusalem;
    come sing your songs of joy and triumph,
    see that your God reigns.
      Awake, awake . . .

2 Burst into songs of joy together,
    O Jerusalem;
    the Lord has comforted His people,
    the redeemed Jerusalem.
      Awake, awake . . .

47 Away in a manger

CRADLE SONG   11 11 11 11

Words: verses 1, 2 unknown
verse 3 J T McFarland (c1906)
Music: W J Kirkpatrick (1838–1921)

1 Away in a manger, no crib for a bed,
   the little Lord Jesus laid down His sweet head;
   the stars in the bright sky looked down where He lay;
   the little Lord Jesus asleep in the hay.

2 The cattle are lowing, the Baby awakes,
   but little Lord Jesus, no crying He makes:
   I love You, Lord Jesus! look down from the sky
   and stay by my side until morning is nigh.

3 Be near me, Lord Jesus; I ask You to stay
   close by me for ever and love me, I pray;
   bless all the dear children in Your tender care,
   and fit us for heaven to live with You there.

48   Be still and know

Words and music: Unknown
Music arranged Roland Fudge

1   Be still and know that I am God.
     Be still and know that I am God.
     Be still and know that I am God.

2   I am the Lord that healeth thee.
     I am the Lord that healeth thee.
     I am the Lord that healeth thee.

3   In Thee, O Lord, I put my trust.
     In Thee, O Lord, I put my trust.
     In Thee, O Lord, I put my trust.

49 Be bold, be strong

Words and music: Morris Chapman
Music arranged Andy Silver

Be bold,___ be strong,___ for the

Lord your God is with___ you;___ be bold,___

be strong, for the Lord your God is with

___ you!_ I am not a-fraid, (No! No! No!)

50 Be still, for the presence of the Lord

Words and music: David J Evans

Words and music: © 1986 Thankyou Music,
PO Box 75, Eastbourne, East Sussex BN23 6NW, UK

pre-sence of the Lord,   the   Ho - ly   One,   is   here.

1 Be still,
     for the presence of the Lord,
      the Holy One, is here;
    come bow before Him now
    with reverence and fear:
    in Him no sin is found –
    we stand on holy ground.
    Be still,
     for the presence of the Lord,
      the Holy One, is here.

2 Be still,
     for the glory of the Lord
      is shining all around;
    He burns with holy fire,
    with splendour He is crowned:
    how awesome is the sight –
    our radiant King of light!
    Be still,
     for the glory of the Lord
      is shining all around.

3 Be still,
     for the power of the Lord
      is moving in this place:
    He comes to cleanse and heal,
    to minister His grace –
    no work too hard for Him.
    In faith receive from Him.
    Be still,
     for the power of the Lord
      is moving in this place.

51 Be Thou my vision

SLANE   10 10 10 10 (Irregular)

Words: from the Irish
tr. Mary Elizabeth Byrne (1880–1931)
Versified by Eleanor Henrietta Hull (1860–1935)
Music: Irish traditional melody
arranged M E F Shaw (1875–1958)

Music arrangement: © Oxford University Press
From *Enlarged Songs of Praise*

1   Be Thou my vision, O Lord of my heart;
    naught be all else to me, save that Thou art –
    Thou my best thought, by day or by night, *in the day or the night*
    waking or sleeping, Thy presence my light.

2   Be Thou my wisdom, *Be* Thou my true Word;
    I ever with Thee, Thou with me, Lord;
    Thou my great Father, I Thy true son;
    Thou in me dwelling, and I with Thee one.

    breastplate my.   inst.
3   Be Thou my battle-shield, sword for the fight,
armour be Thou my dignity, Thou my delight. *Might*
    Thou my soul's shelter, Thou my high tower:
    raise Thou me heavenward, O Power of my power.

    need   inst
4   Riches I heed not, nor man's empty praise,
    Thou mine inheritance, now and always:
    Thou and Thou only, first in my heart,
    High King of heaven, my treasure Thou art.

                        the battle is done
5   High King of heaven, after victory won,
    may I reach heaven's joys, O bright heaven's Sun!
Christ — Heart of my own heart, whatever befall,
    still be my vision, O ruler of all.
                    Thou.

*New arrangement
Side 1. last one
on Sweet rain.*

Because He lives

Words: Gloria and William J Gaither
Music: William J Gaither

1 God sent His Son, they called Him Je - sus;
2 How sweet to hold a new-born ba - by,
3 And then one day I'll cross the ri - ver;

— He came to love, heal, and for - give;
— and feel the pride and joy he gives;
— I'll fight life's fi - nal war with pain;

— He lived and died to buy my par - don,
— but great - er still the calm as - sur - ance,
— and then as death gives way to vic - tory,

— an emp - ty grave is there to prove my Sav-iour lives.
— this child can face un-cer-tain days be-cause He lives.
— I'll see the lights of glo - ry and I'll know He lives.

53 Because Your love is better than life

Words and music: Phil Potter
Music arranged Andrew Maries

1 Be-cause Your love_____ is bet-ter than life, with my lips I will glo-ri-fy__ You; I will praise You_____ as long as I live, in Your name_____ I lift my hands._____

HARMONY

F (E)   **Gm** (F#m)

2 Be-cause Your Son_____ has giv-en me life,
3 Be-cause Your Spi - rit_____ is fill-ing my life, with my
4 Be-cause Your love_____ is bet-ter than life,

C7 (B7)   **B♭/F** (A/E)   **F** (E)   **F#dim** (Fdim)

lips I will glo - ri - fy___ You, I will praise You___ as long as I

Gm (F#m)   **C7** (B7)   **F** (E)

live, in Your name_____ I lift my hands._____

OPTIONAL INSTRUMENTAL PART

(Voices)

54 Bind us together, Lord

Words and music: Bob Gillman
Music arranged Norman Warren

Bind us to-geth-er, Lord, bind us to-geth-er with
cords that can-not be bro - ken; bind us to-geth-er, Lord,
bind us to-geth-er, O bind us to-geth-er with love.

1 There is on - ly one God, there is on - ly one
2 Made for the glo - ry of God, pur-chased by His pre-cious
3 You are the fam - ily of God, You are the pro - mise di -

King,   there___ is   on - ly   one   Bo - dy =___
Son.   Born with the right to   be   clean,_____   for
- vine,   You are God's cho - sen de - sire,____

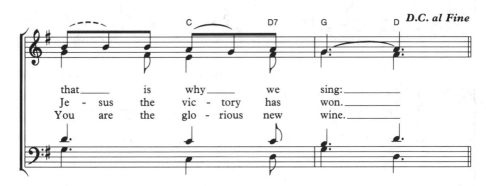

D.C. al Fine

that____   is   why____   we   sing:_____
Je - sus   the   vic - tory has   won.____
You are   the   glo - rious new   wine.____

Bind us together, Lord,
bind us together
with cords that cannot be broken;
bind us together, Lord,
bind us together,
O bind us together with love.

1   There is only one God,
     there is only one King,
     there is only one Body –
     that is why we sing:
       Bind us together . . .

2   Made for the glory of God,
     purchased by His precious Son.
     Born with the right to be clean,
     for Jesus the victory has won.
       Bind us together . . .

3   You are the family of God,
     You are the promise divine,
     You are God's chosen desire,
     You are the glorious new wine.
       Bind us together . . .

55 Beneath the cross of Jesus

St Christopher 76 86 86 86

Words: Elizabeth Clephane (1830–69)
Music: Frederick C Maker (1844–1927)

1 Be - neath the cross of Je - sus I fain would take my stand –
2 Up - on that cross of Je - sus mine eye at times can see
3 I take, O cross, thy sha - dow, for my a - bid - ing - place!

the sha - dow of a migh - ty rock with - in a wea - ry land;
the ve - ry dy - ing form of One who suf - fered there for me;
I ask no o - ther sun - shine than the sun - shine of His face;

a home with - in a wil - der - ness, a rest up - on the way,
and from my strick - en heart, with tears, two won - ders I con - fess –
con - tent to let the world go by, to know no gain or loss –

from the burn - ing of the noon - tide heat and the bur - den of the day.
the__ won - ders of re - deem - ing love, and__ my own worth - less - ness.
my__ sin - ful self my on - ly shame, my__ glo - ry all - the cross.

56 Bless the Lord, O my soul

BLESS THE LORD

Words and music: Andrea Crouch

57   Bless the Lord, O my soul

Words: from Psalm 103
Music: Unknown
arranged Roland Fudge

Blessed are the pure in heart

Words and music: Betty Lou Mills
Music arranged Christopher Norton

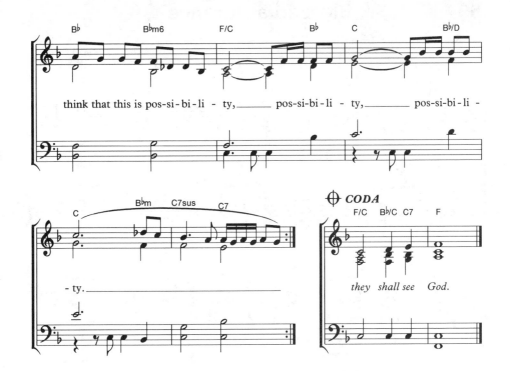

think that this is pos-si-bi-li - ty,_____ pos-si-bi-li - ty,_____ pos-si-bi-li - ty._____

CODA

they shall see God.

Blessed are the pure in heart,
for they shall see God;
blessed are the pure in heart,
for they shall see God.

1 To see God, the alpha and omega,
   to see God, creator, life-sustainer,
   to see God, to think that this is possibility.
   Blessed are . . .

2 To see God, the everlasting Father,
   to see God, whose love endures for ever,
   to see God, how wonderful to think that this could be.
   Blessed are . . .

3 To see God, the God who talked with Moses,
   to see God, whose mercies are so endless,
   to see God, what better incentive for purity.
   Blessed are . . .

4 To see God, the One I've loved and longed for,
   to see God, the Father of my Saviour,
   to see God, a dream come true, at last His face I'll see.
   Blessed are . . .

59 Blessed assurance

BLESSED ASSURANCE   Irregular

Words: Frances van Alstyne (1820–1915)
(Fanny J Crosby)
Music: Phoebe Palmer Knapp (1839–1908)

Bless-ed as - sur - ance, Je - sus is mine:___ O what a

fore - taste of glo-ry di - vine!___ Heir of sal - va - tion, pur-chase of

God;___ born of His Spi - rit, washed in His blood.___

This is my sto - ry, this is my song,___ prais-ing my

Sav - iour all the day long.___ This is my sto - ry, this is my

song,___ prais-ing my Sav - iour all the day long.___

1 Blessed assurance, Jesus is mine:
   O what a foretaste of glory divine!
   Heir of salvation, purchase of God;
   born of His Spirit, washed in His blood.
     This is my story, this is my song,
     praising my Saviour all the day long;
     this is my story, this is my song,
     praising my Saviour all the day long.

2 Perfect submission, perfect delight,
   visions of rapture burst on my sight;
   angels descending, bring from above
   echoes of mercy, whispers of love.
     This is my story . . .

3 Perfect submission, all is at rest,
   I in my Saviour am happy and blest;
   watching and waiting, looking above,
   filled with His goodness, lost in His love.
     This is my story . . .

60 Blest be the tie that binds

DENNIS   SM

Words: John Fawcett(1740–1817) altd.
Music: J G Nägeli (1768–1836)
arranged Phil Burt

Blest be the tie that binds our hearts in Christ - ian love; the fel - low - ship of kin - dred minds is like to that a - bove.

1 Blest be the tie that binds
   our hearts in Christian love;
   the fellowship of kindred minds
   is like to that above.

2 Before our Father's throne
   we pour our ardent prayers;
   our fears, our hopes, our aims are one,
   our comforts and our cares.

3 We share our mutual woes,
   our mutual burdens bear,
   and often for each other flows
   the sympathizing tear.

4 When for awhile we part,
   this thought will soothe our pain,
   that we shall still be joined in heart,
   and hope to meet again.

5 This glorious hope revives
   our courage by the way,
   while each in expectation lives,
   and longs to see the day.

6 From sorrow, toil, and pain,
   and sin we shall be free;
   and perfect love and friendship reign
   through all eternity.

61   Born by the Holy Spirit's breath

WHITSUN PSALM   LM

Words: From Romans 8
Timothy Dudley-Smith
Music: Noël Tredinnick

1 Born by the Holy Spirit's breath,
loosed from the law of sin and death,
now cleared in Christ from every claim,
no judgement stands against our name.

2 In us the Spirit makes His home
that we in Him may overcome;
Christ's risen life, in all its powers,
its all-prevailing strength, is ours.

3 Sons, then, and heirs of God most high,
we by His Spirit 'Father' cry;
that Spirit with our spirit shares
to frame and breathe our wordless prayers.

4 One is His love, His purpose one:
to form the likeness of His Son
in all who, called and justified,
shall reign in glory at His side.

5 Nor death nor life, nor powers unseen,
nor height nor depth can come between;
we know through peril, pain and sword,
the love of God in Christ our Lord.

62 Born in the night

MARY'S CHILD

Words and music: Geoffrey Ainger

Born___ in the night, Ma - ry's child, a
long way from Your home;___ com - ing in need,
Ma - ry's child, born___ in a bor - rowed room.

1 Born in the night,
　　Mary's child,
　a long way from Your home;
　coming in need,
　　Mary's child,
　born in a borrowed room.

2 Clear shining light,
　　Mary's child,
　Your face lights up our way:
　light of the world,
　　Mary's child,
　dawn on our darkened day.

3 Truth of our life,
　　Mary's child,
　You tell us God is good:
　prove it is true,
　　Mary's child,
　go to Your cross of wood.

4 Hope of the world,
　　Mary's child,
　You're coming soon to reign:
　King of the earth,
　　Mary's child,
　walk in our streets again.

63 Break forth into joy

Words and music: Anon
Music arranged Roland Fudge

Break forth in - to joy O my soul;_____ break

forth in - to joy O my soul. In the

pre-sence of the Lord there is joy for ev - er-more; break

forth,_____ break forth__ in - to joy.

64   Break Thou the bread of life

LATHBURY   64 64 D

Words: Mary A Lathbury (1841–1913)
and Alexander Groves (1843–1909)
Music: William F Sherwin (1826–88)

Break Thou the bread of life, dear Lord to me,

as Thou didst break the bread be - side the___ sea;

be - yond the sa - cred page I seek Thee, Lord;___

my spi - rit longs for Thee, Thou liv - ing Word!

1 Break Thou the bread of life,
    dear Lord to me,
  as Thou didst break the bread
    beside the sea;
  beyond the sacred page
    I seek Thee, Lord;
  my spirit longs for Thee,
    Thou living Word!

2 Thou art the bread of life,
    O Lord, to me,
  Thy holy word the truth
    that saveth me;
  give me to eat and live
    with Thee above,
  teach me to love Thy truth,
    for Thou art love.

3 O send Thy Spirit, Lord,
    now unto me,
  that He may touch my eyes,
    and make me see;
  show me the truth concealed
    within Thy word,
  and in Thy book revealed
    I see Thee, Lord.

4 Bless Thou the bread of life
    to me, to me,
  as Thou didst bless the loaves
    by Galilee;
  then shall all bondage cease,
    all fetters fall,
  and I shall find my peace,
    my all in all!

65 Brightest and best

EPIPHANY HYMN   11 10 11 10

Words: Reginald Heber (1783–1826)
Music: J F Thrupp (1827–67)

Bright - est and best of the sons of the morn - ing,
dawn on our dark - ness and lend us thine aid;
star of the east__ the ho - ri - zon a - dor - ing,__
guide__ where our in - fant Re - deem - er is laid.

1 Brightest and best of the sons of the morning,
   dawn on our darkness and lend us thine aid;
   star of the east the horizon adoring,
   guide where our infant Redeemer is laid.

2 Cold on His cradle the dew-drops are shining;
   low lies His head with the beasts of the stall:
   angels adore Him, in slumber reclining,
   maker and monarch, and Saviour of all.

3 Say, shall we yield Him, in costly devotion,
   odours of Edom, and offerings divine;
   gems of the mountain, and pearls of the ocean,
   myrrh from the forest, or gold from the mine?

4 Vainly we offer each ample oblation;
   vainly with gifts would His favour secure;
   richer by far is the heart's adoration;
   dearer to God are the prayers of the poor.

5 Brightest and best of the sons of the morning,
   dawn on our darkness and lend us thine aid;
   star of the east the horizon adorning,
   guide where our infant Redeemer is laid.

Broken for me

Words and music: Janet Lunt

Gently

Capo 2(D)

Bro-ken for me,_____ bro-ken for you,_____ the bo-dy of Je - sus_____ bro-ken for you. He of-fered His bo-dy,_____ He poured out His soul,

Words and music: © 1978 Mustard Seed Music,
PO Box 356, Leighton Buzzard LU7 8WP

♦ CODA

Je-sus was bro - ken_____ that we might be whole: *Bro-ken for* _____ *bro-ken for you.*

Broken for me, broken for you,
the body of Jesus broken for you.

1 He offered His body, He poured out His soul,
   Jesus was broken that we might be whole:
       Broken for me . . .

2 Come to My table and with Me dine,
   eat of My bread and drink of My wine:
       Broken for me . . .

3 This is My body given for you,
   eat it remembering I died for you:
       Broken for me . . .

4 This is My blood I shed for you,
   for your forgiveness, making you new:
       Broken for me . . .

67   Breathe on me, breath of God

Words: Edwin Hatch (1835–89)
Music: Robert Jackson (1840–1914)

1   Breathe on me, breath of God,
fill me with life anew,
that I may love what Thou dost love,
and do what Thou wouldst do.

2   Breathe on me, breath of God,
until my heart is pure,
until with Thee I will one will,
to do and to endure.

3   Breathe on me, breath of God,
till I am wholly Thine,
until this earthly part of me
glows with Thy fire divine.

4   Breathe on me, breath of God,
so shall I never die,
but live with Thee the perfect life
of Thine eternity.

68 Cause me to come

Words and music: R Edward Miller

Thoughtfully

1 Cause me to come to Thy river, O Lord, (*3 times*)
   cause me to come, cause me to drink, cause me to live.

2 Cause me to drink from Thy river, O Lord, (*3 times*)
   cause me to come, cause me to drink, cause me to live.

3 Cause me to live by Thy river, O Lord, (*3 times*)
   cause me to come, cause me to drink, cause me to live.

69

Change my heart, O God

Words and music: Eddie Espinosa
Music arranged David Peacock

70 Children of Jerusalem

CHILDREN'S PRAISE   77 77 with refrain

Words: John Henley (1800–42)
Music: from Curwen's *Tune Book*, 1842

Child-ren of Je - ru-sa-lem sang the praise of Je - sus' name;

child - ren, too, of mo - dern days, join to sing the

Sav-iour's praise: *Hark! hark! hark! while child-ren's voi-ces sing,*

Hark! hark! hark! while child-ren's voi-ces sing loud ho-san-nas,

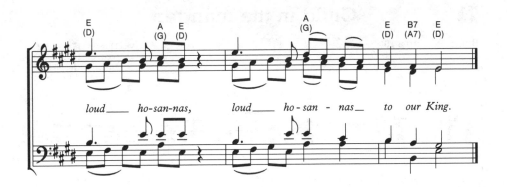

loud___ ho-san-nas,   loud___ ho - san - nas___   to   our King.

1   Children of Jerusalem
     sang the praise of Jesus' name;
     children, too, of modern days,
     join to sing the Saviour's praise:
        Hark, hark, hark! while children's voices sing,
        hark, hark, hark! while children's voices sing
        loud hosannas, loud hosannas,
        loud hosannas to our King.

2   We are taught to love the Lord,
     we are taught to read His word,
     we are taught the way to heaven;
     praise for all to God be given:
        Hark, hark, hark . . .

3   Parents, teachers, old and young,
     all unite to swell the song;
     higher and yet higher rise,
     till hosannas reach the skies:
        Hark, hark, hark . . .

71   Child in the manger

BUNESSAN   10 8 10 8

Words: after M MacDonald (1789–1872)
L Macbean (1853–1931)
Music: Gaelic melody
arranged Phil Burt

Gently

Child in the man - ger, in - fant of Ma - ry, out - cast and

stran - ger, Lord of all! Child who in - her - its all our trans -

- gress - ions, all our de - mer - its on__ Him fall.

1   Child in the manger, infant of Mary,
outcast and stranger, Lord of all!
Child who inherits all our transgressions,
all our demerits on Him fall.

2   Once the most holy child of salvation
gentle and lowly lived below:
now as our glorious mighty Redeemer,
see Him victorious over each foe.

3   Prophets foretold Him, infant of wonder;
angels behold Him on His throne:
worthy our Saviour of all their praises;
happy for ever are His own.

72 Christ is the answer

Words and music: Major T W Maltby

Christ is the answer to my every need;
Christ is the answer, He is my friend indeed.
Problems of life my spirit may assail,
with Christ my Saviour I need never fail,
for Christ is the answer to my need.

73   Christ is made the sure foundation

WESTMINSTER ABBEY   87 87 87

Words: from the Latin, J M Neale (1818–66)
in this version Jubilate Hymns
Music: H Purcell (1659–95)

Christ is made the sure foun - da - tion,

Christ the head and cor - ner - stone cho - sen

of the Lord and pre - cious, bind - ing all the

Church in one; ho - ly Zi - on's help for

ev - er, and her con - fi - dence___ a - lone.

1 Christ is made the sure foundation,
  Christ the head and corner-stone
  chosen of the Lord and precious,
  binding all the Church in one;
  holy Zion's help for ever,
  and her confidence alone.

2 All within that holy city
  dearly loved of God on high,
  in exultant jubilation
  sing, in perfect harmony;
  God the One-in-Three adoring
  in glad hymns eternally.

3 We as living stones invoke you:
  Come among us, Lord, today!
  with Your gracious loving-kindness
  hear Your children as we pray;
  and the fulness of Your blessing
  in our fellowship display.

4 Here entrust to all Your servants
  what we long from You to gain –
  that on earth and in the heavens
  we one people shall remain,
  till united in Your glory
  evermore with You we reign.

5 Praise and honour to the Father,
  praise and honour to the Son,
  praise and honour to the Spirit,
  ever Three and ever One:
  one in power and one in glory
  while eternal ages run.

74 Christ is risen! hallelujah

MORGENLIED   87 87 D with refrain

Words: John Samuel Bewley Monsell (1811–75)
Music: Frederick Charles Maker (1844–1927)

Christ is ris-en! hal-le-lu-jah! ris-en our vic-tor-ious Head;

sing His prais-es; hal-le-lu-jah! Christ is ris-en from the dead.

Grate-ful-ly our hearts a-dore Him, as His light once more ap-pears;

bow-ing down in joy be-fore Him, ris-ing up from grief and tears.

Christ is ris-en! hal-le-lu-jah! ris-en our vic-tor-ious Head;

sing His prais-es; hal-le-lu-jah! Christ is ris-en from the dead.

1 Christ is risen! hallelujah!
  risen our victorious Head;
  sing His praises; hallelujah!
  Christ is risen from the dead.
  Gratefully our hearts adore Him,
  as His light once more appears;
  bowing down in joy before Him,
  rising up from grief and tears.
      Christ is risen! hallelujah!
      risen our victorious Head;
      sing His praises; hallelujah!
      Christ is risen from the dead.

2 Christ is risen! all the sadness
  of His earthly life is o'er;
  through the open gates of gladness
  He returns to life once more.
  Death and hell before Him bending,
  He doth rise the victor now,
  angels on His steps attending,
  glory round His wounded brow.
      Christ is risen! . . .

3 Christ is risen! henceforth never
  death or hell shall us enthral;
  we are Christ's, in Him for ever
  we have triumphed over all;
  all the doubting and dejection
  of our trembling hearts have ceased.
  'Tis His day of resurrection;
  let us rise and keep the feast.
      Christ is risen! . . .

75 Christ is surely coming

LAND OF HOPE AND GLORY 11 11 11 11 11

Words: from Revelation 22
Christopher Idle
Music: Edward Elgar (1857–1934)
arranged Robin Sheldon

Christ is sure-ly com-ing, bring-ing His re-ward,

O - me - ga and Al - pha, First and Last and Lord;

root and stem of Da - vid, bril-liant Morn-ing Star –

Meet your Judge and Sav - iour, na-tions near and far;

meet your Judge and Sav - iour, na-tions near and far!

1 Christ is surely coming, bringing His reward,
  Omega and Alpha, First and Last and Lord;
  root and stem of David, brilliant Morning Star –
     Meet your Judge and Saviour, nations near and far;
     meet your Judge and Saviour, nations near and far!

2 See the holy city! There they enter in,
  men by Christ made holy, washed from every sin;
  thirsty ones, desiring all He loves to give:
     Come for living water, freely drink, and live;
     come for living water, freely drink, and live!

3 Grace be with God's people! Praise His holy name –
  Father, Son, and Spirit, evermore the same!
  Hear the certain promise from the eternal home:
     'Surely I come quickly!' – Come, Lord Jesus, come;
     'Surely I come quickly!' – Come, Lord Jesus, come!

76   Christ the Lord is risen today

EASTER HYMN   77 77 with Hallelujahs

Words: Charles Wesley (1707–88)
Music: *Lyra Davidica*, 1708
arranged W A Monk (1823–89)

Christ the Lord is risen to-day;— Hal - - le - lu - jah!

sons of men and an - gels say:— Hal - - le - lu - jah!

raise your joys and— tri-umphs high; Hal - - le - lu - jah!

sing, ye heavens; thou earth, re - ply:— Hal - - le - lu - jah!

1 Christ the Lord is risen today;
     Hallelujah!
   sons of men and angels say:
   raise your joys and triumphs high;
   sing, ye heavens; thou earth, reply:

2 Love's redeeming work is done,
   fought the fight, the battle won;
   Lo! our sun's eclipse is o'er,
   Lo! He sets in blood no more:

3 Vain the stone, the watch, the seal;
   Christ hath burst the gates of hell;
   death in vain forbids Him rise;
   Christ hath opened paradise;

4 Lives again our glorious King;
   where, O death, is now thy sting?
   Once He died our souls to save;
   where thy victory, O grave?

5 Soar we now where Christ hath led,
   following our exalted Head;
   made like Him, like Him we rise;
   ours the cross, the grave, the skies:

6 Hail the Lord of earth and heaven,
   praise to Thee by both be given:
   Thee we greet, in triumph sing
   Hail, our resurrected King:

77 Christ triumphant

CHRIST TRIUMPHANT   85 85 79

Words: Michael Saward
Music: Michael Baughen

1 Christ triumphant, ever reigning,
   Saviour, Master, King,
   Lord of heaven, our lives sustaining,
   hear us as we sing:
     Yours the glory and the crown,
     the high renown, the eternal name.

2 Word incarnate, truth revealing,
   Son of Man on earth!
   power and majesty concealing
   by your humble birth:
     Yours the glory . . .

3 Suffering servant, scorned, ill-treated,
   victim crucified!
   death is through the cross defeated,
   sinners justified:
     Yours the glory . . .

4 Priestly King, enthroned for ever
   high in heaven above!
   sin and death and hell shall never
   stifle hymns of love:
     Yours the glory . . .

5 So, our hearts and voices raising
   through the ages long,
   ceaselessly upon You gazing,
   this shall be our song:
     Yours the glory . . .

78 Christ the Way of life possess me

Words: Timothy Dudley-Smith
Music: Phil Burt

Christ the Way of life pos-sess me, lift my heart to love and praise; guide and keep, sus-tain and bless me, all my days, all my days.

1 Christ the Way of life possess me,
  lift my heart to love and praise;
  guide and keep, sustain and bless me,
  all my days, all my days.

2 Well of life, for ever flowing,
  make my barren soul and bare
  like a watered garden growing
  fresh and fair, fresh and fair.

3 May the Tree of life in splendour
  from its leafy boughs impart
  grace divine and healing tender,
  strength of heart, strength of heart.

4 Path of life before me shining,
  let me come when earth is past,
  sorrow, self and sin resigning,
  home at last, home at last.

79   Christ, whose glory fills the skies

RATISBON   77 77 77

Words: Charles Wesley (1707–88)
Music: melody from J G Werner's *Choralbuch*, Leipzig, 1815
arranged W H Havergal (1793–1870)

Christ, whose glo-ry fills the skies, Christ, the true, the on-ly light,

Sun of right-eous-ness, a-rise, tri-umph o'er_ the shades of night:

Day-spring from on high, be_ near; Day-star, in my heart ap-pear.

1   Christ, whose glory fills the skies,
Christ, the true, the only light,
Sun of righteousness, arise,
triumph o'er the shades of night:
Day-spring from on high, be near;
Day-star, in my heart appear.

2   Dark and cheerless is the morn
unaccompanied by Thee;
joyless is the day's return,
till Thy mercy's beams I see;
till they inward light impart,
glad my eyes, and warm my heart.

3   Visit then this soul of mine;
pierce the gloom of sin and grief;
fill me, radiancy divine;
scatter all my unbelief;
more and more Thyself display,
shining to the perfect day.

80 Christians awake!

YORKSHIRE   10 10 10 10 10 10

Words: John Byrom (1692–1763) altd.
Music: John Wainwright (1723–68)

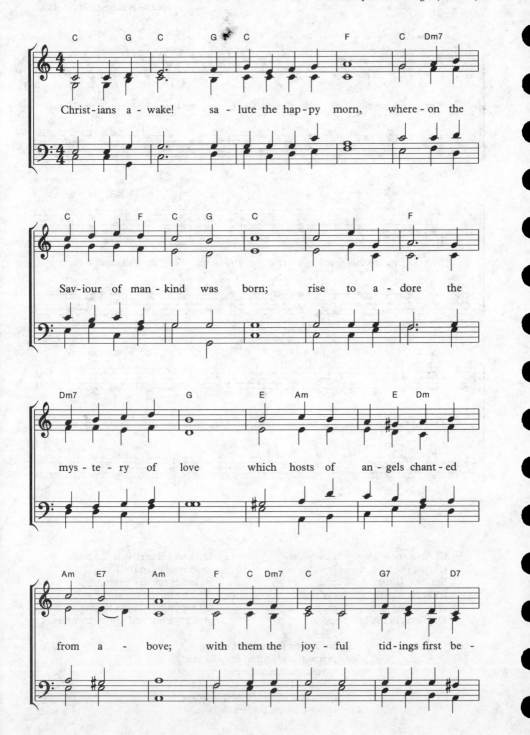

Christ-ians a-wake! sa-lute the hap-py morn, where-on the
Sav-iour of man-kind was born; rise to a-dore the
mys-te-ry of love which hosts of an-gels chant-ed
from a-bove; with them the joy-ful tid-ings first be-

-gun of God in - car-nate, and the Vir - gin's Son.

1 Christians awake! salute the happy morn,
   whereon the Saviour of mankind was born;
   rise to adore the mystery of love
   which hosts of angels chanted from above;
   with them the joyful tidings first begun
   of God incarnate, and the Virgin's Son.

2 Then to the watchful shepherds it was told,
   who heard the angelic herald's voice 'Behold,
   I bring good tidings of a Saviour's birth
   to you and all the nations upon earth:
   this day hath God fulfilled His promised word,
   this day is born a Saviour, Christ the Lord.'

3 He spake; and straightway the celestial choir,
   in hymns of joy unknown before conspire;
   the praises of redeeming love they sang,
   and heaven's whole orb with hallelujahs rang:
   God's highest glory was their anthem still,
   'On earth be peace, and unto men goodwill.'

4 To Bethlehem straight the enlightened shepherds ran,
   to see the wonder God had wrought for man;
   then to their flocks, still praising God, return,
   and their glad hearts with holy rapture burn;
   amazed, the wondrous tidings they proclaim,
   the first apostles of His infant fame.

5 Then may we hope, the angelic hosts among,
   to sing, redeemed, a glad triumphal song:
   He that was born upon this joyful day
   around us all His glory shall display;
   saved by His love, incessant we shall sing
   eternal praise to heaven's almighty King.

81   Clap your hands, you people all

EPHRAIM   77 77

Words: Charles Wesley (1707–88)
Music: Henry Leslie (c1825–76)

Clap your hands, you peo-ple all, praise the God on whom you call;

lift your voice, and shout His praise, tri-umph in His sove-reign grace!

1   Clap your hands, you people all,
    praise the God on whom you call;
    lift your voice, and shout His praise,
    triumph in His sovereign grace!

2   Glorious is the Lord Most High,
    terrible in majesty;
    He His sovereign sway maintains,
    King o'er all the earth He reigns.

3   Jesus is gone up on high,
    takes His seat above the sky:
    shout the angel-choirs aloud,
    echoing to the trump of God.

4   Sons of earth, the triumph join,
    praise Him with the host divine;
    emulate the heavenly powers,
    their victorious Lord is ours.

5   Shout the God enthroned above,
    trumpet forth His conquering love;
    praises to our Jesus sing,
    praises to our glorious King!

6   Power is all to Jesus given,
    power o'er hell, and earth, and heaven!
    Power He now to us imparts;
    praise Him with believing hearts.

7   Wonderful in saving power,
    Him let all our hearts adore;
    earth and heaven repeat the cry,
    'Glory be to God most high!'

82 Cleanse me from my sin

Words and music: R Hudson Pope (1879–1967)

Cleanse me from my sin, Lord, put Thy power with-in, Lord,

take me as I am, Lord, and make me all Thine own.

Keep me day by day, Lord, un-der-neath Thy sway, Lord,

make my heart Thy pal-ace, and Thy roy-al throne.

83   Come and join the celebration

CELEBRATIONS   11 14 with refrain

Words and music: Valerie Collison

Come and join the ce-le-bra-tion, it's a ve-ry spe-cial day;

come and share our ju-bi-la-tion, there's a new King born to-day!

1 See the shep-herds hur-ry down to Beth-le-hem;

gaze in won-der at the Son of God who lay be-fore them.

Words and music: © 1972 High-Fye Music Ltd, Campbell Connelly Co Ltd,
8–9 Frith Street, London W1V 5TZ

Come and join the ce-le-bra-tion, it's a ve-ry spe-cial day;

come and share our ju-bi-la-tion, there's a new King born to-day!

2 Wise men jour-ney, led to wor-ship by a star,
3 'God is with us,' 'round the world the mes-sage bring;

2nd time **D.C. al Fine**

kneel in hom-age, bring-ing pre-cious gifts from lands a-far, so
He is with us, 'Wel-come!' all the bells on earth are peal-ing.

84   Come and praise the living God

Words and music: Mike Kerry
Music arranged Roland Fudge

Triumphantly

Come and praise the liv-ing God, come___ and wor-ship,

come___ and wor-ship. He has made you priest and king,

last time **to Coda**

come___ and wor-ship the liv-ing God.___ We

come not to a moun-tain of fire and smoke,
By___ His___ voice He shakes the earth,___ His

not to gloom and dark-ness or trum - pet sound; we
judge - ments_ known through - out the world. But

come to the new_ Je - ru-sa - lem, the ho - ly ci - ty of God.
we have a ci - ty that for ev - er stands, the ho - ly ci - ty of God.

D.C.

⊕ *CODA*

liv-ing God._____

Come and praise the living God,
come and worship, come and worship.
He has made you priest and king,
come and worship the living God.

1   We come not to a mountain of fire and smoke,
not to gloom and darkness or trumpet sound;
we come to the new Jerusalem,
the holy city of God.
    Come and praise . . .

2   By His voice He shakes the earth,
His judgements known throughout the world.
But we have a city that for ever stands,
the holy city of God.
    Come and praise . . .

85

Come and see

Words and music: Graham Kendrick
Music arranged Christopher Norton

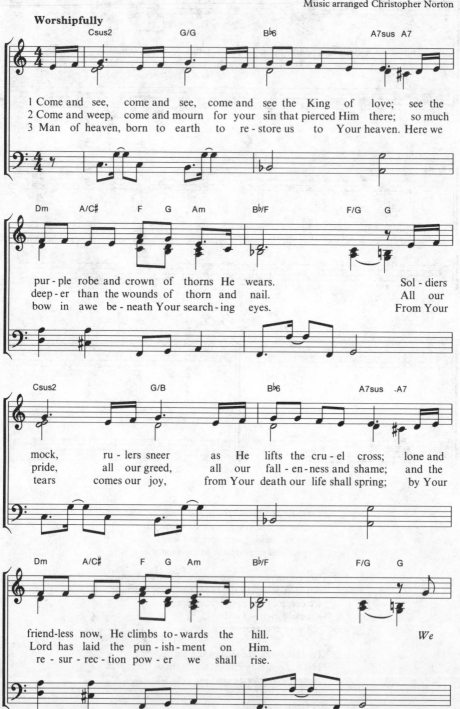

Worshipfully

1 Come and see, come and see, come and see the King of love; see the
2 Come and weep, come and mourn for your sin that pierced Him there; so much
3 Man of heaven, born to earth to re-store us to Your heaven. Here we

pur-ple robe and crown of thorns He wears. Sol-diers
deep-er than the wounds of thorn and nail. All our
bow in awe be-neath Your search-ing eyes. From Your

mock, ru-lers sneer as He lifts the cru-el cross; lone and
pride, all our greed, all our fall-en-ness and shame; and the
tears comes our joy, from Your death our life shall spring; by Your

friend-less now, He climbs to-wards the hill. *We*
Lord has laid the pun-ish-ment on Him.
re-sur-rec-tion pow-er we shall rise.

86 Come and see the shining hope

MARCHING THROUGH GEORGIA   13 13 13 8 10 10 13 8

Words: from Revelation 4 and 5
Christopher Idle
Music: American traditional melody
arranged David Wilson

Come and see the shin-ing hope that Christ's a-pos-tle saw;

on the earth, con-fu-sion, but in heaven an op-en door,

where the liv-ing crea-tures praise the Lamb for ev-er-more: Love has the vic-tory for

ev - er! *Am - en, He comes! to bring His own re-ward!* A-

- men, praise God! for jus-tice now re-stored; king-doms of the world be-come the

king-doms of the Lord: Love has the vic-tory for ev - er!

1 Come and see the shining hope that Christ's apostle saw;
on the earth, confusion, but in heaven an open door,
where the living creatures praise the Lamb for evermore:
Love has the victory for ever!
  Amen, He comes!
  to bring His own reward!
  Amen, praise God!
  for justice now restored;
  kingdoms of the world
  become the kingdoms of the Lord:
  Love has the victory for ever!

2 All the gifts You send us, Lord, are faithful, good, and true;
holiness and righteousness are shown in all You do:
who can see Your greatest Gift and fail to worship You?
Love has the victory for ever!
  Amen, He comes . . .

3 Power and salvation all belong to God on high!
So the mighty multitudes of heaven make their cry,
singing Alleluia! where the echoes never die:
Love has the victory for ever!
  Amen, He comes . . .

87 Come and praise Him

Words and music: A Carter
Music arranged Roger Mayor

With majesty

Come and praise Him,___ roy - al priest - hood,___ come and wor - ship,___ ho - ly na - tion,___ wor-ship Je - sus,___ our Re - deem - er,___ He is pre - cious,___ King of glo - ry.

Come bless the Lord

Words: from Psalm 134
Music: Anon
arranged Roger Mayor

Come bless the Lord, all ye ser-vants of the
Lord, who stand by night
in the house of the Lord; lift up your
hands in the ho-ly place,
come bless the Lord, come bless the Lord._____

89   Come down, O love divine

DOWN AMPNEY   6 6 11 D

Words: after Bianco da Siena
R F Littledale (1833–90)
Music: R Vaughan Williams (1872–1958)

1 Come down, O love divine,
   seek Thou this soul of mine
   and visit it with Thine own ardour glowing;
   O Comforter, draw near,
   within my heart appear,
   and kindle it, Thy holy flame bestowing.

2 O let it freely burn,
   till earthly passions turn
   to dust and ashes, in its heat consuming;
   and let Thy glorious light
   shine ever on my sight,
   and clothe me round, the while my path illuming.

3 Let holy charity
   mine outward vesture be,
   and lowliness become mine inner clothing;
   true lowliness of heart,
   which takes the humbler part,
   and o'er its own shortcomings weeps with loathing.

4 And so the yearning strong,
   with which the soul will long,
   shall far outpass the power of human telling;
   for none can guess its grace,
   till he become the place
   wherein the Holy Spirit makes His dwelling.

90 Come, Holy Ghost

Veni Creator   LM

Words: after R Maurus (c776–856)
J Cosin (1594–1672)
Music: from proper plainsong melody
arranged Roland Fudge

Flowing

Come, Ho - ly Ghost, our souls__ in - spire,

and light-en with__ ce - les - tial fire: Thou the__ a - noint - ing

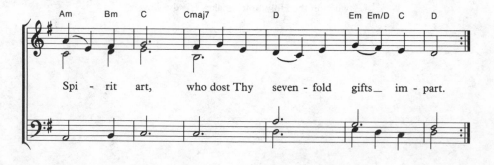

Spi - rit art, who dost Thy seven - fold gifts__ im - part.

After verse 4

Praise_____ to Thy__ e - ter - nal me - rit,

Fa - ther, Son,_ and Ho - ly Spi-rit! A - men.

1 Come, Holy Ghost, our souls inspire,
and lighten with celestial fire:
Thou the anointing Spirit art,
who dost Thy sevenfold gifts impart.

2 Thy blessèd unction from above
is comfort, life, and fire of love:
enable with perpetual light
the dullness of our blinded sight.

3 Anoint and cheer our soilèd face
with the abundance of Thy grace:
keep far our foes, give peace at home –
where Thou art guide no ill can come.

4 Teach us to know the Father, Son,
and Thee, of both to be but One;
that, through the ages all along,
this, this may be our endless song:

Praise to Thy eternal merit,
Father, Son, and Holy Spirit! Amen.

91   Come let us bow down in worship

Words and music: Andy Silver

Come let us bow down in wor - ship,

let us kneel be - fore the Lord our Ma - ker.

Come let us bow down in wor - ship, for

He is our God and we are His peo - ple, for

92 Come, let us praise the Lord

66 66 44 44

Words: from Psalm 95
Timothy Dudley-Smith
Music: Chilean folk-song
adapted and arranged Michael Paget

Steadily ♩. = 54

Come, let us praise the Lord, with joy our God acclaim, His greatness tell abroad and bless His saving name.

If sung in harmony, the words of the bass part are the same as for the tune,
but sung to the bass rhythm one syllable to each note.

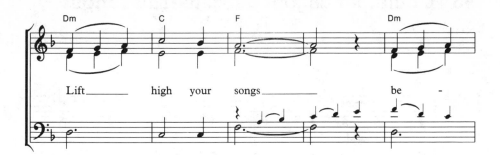

Lift____ high your songs____ be -

- fore__ His throne_____ to whom a -

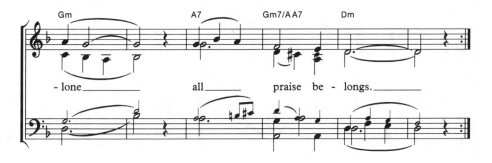

- lone_____ all____ praise be - longs._____

1 Come, let us praise the Lord,
with joy our God acclaim,
His greatness tell abroad
and bless His saving name.
Lift high your songs
before His throne
to whom alone
all praise belongs.

2 Our God of matchless worth,
our King beyond compare,
the deepest bounds of earth,
the hills, are in His care.
He all decrees,
who by His hand
prepared the land
and formed the seas.

3 In worship bow the knee,
our glorious God confess;
the great Creator, He,
the Lord our righteousness.
He reigns unseen:
his flock He feeds
and gently leads
in pastures green.

4 Come, hear His voice today,
receive what love imparts;
His holy will obey
and harden not your hearts.
His ways are best;
and lead at last,
all troubles past,
to perfect rest.

93 Come, let us join our cheerful songs

NATIVITY CM

Words: Isaac Watts (1674–1748)
Music: Henry Lahee (1826–1912)

Come, let us join our cheer - ful songs with an - gels round the throne;___ ten thou - sand thou - sand are their tongues, but all their joys are___ one.

1   Come, let us join our cheerful songs
    with angels round the throne;
    ten thousand thousand are their tongues,
    but all their joys are one.

2   'Worthy the Lamb that died!' they cry,
    'to be exalted thus';
    'Worthy the Lamb!' our lips reply,
    'for He was slain for us.'

3   Jesus is worthy to receive
    honour and power divine;
    and blessings more than we can give
    be, Lord, for ever Thine.

4   The whole creation join in one,
    to bless the sacred name
    of Him that sits upon the throne,
    and to adore the Lamb.

94   Come let us sing

WONDERFUL LOVE   10 4 10 7 4 10

Words: Robert Walmsley (1831–1905)
Music: F Luke Wiseman (1858–1944)

Come let us sing of a won-der-ful love, ten-der and true;____ out of the heart of the Fa-ther a-bove,____ stream-ing to me and to you:____ Won-der-ful

love_____ dwells in the heart of the Fa-ther a - bove.

1 Come let us sing of a wonderful love,
   tender and true;
   out of the heart of the Father above,
   streaming to me and to you:
   Wonderful love
   dwells in the heart of the Father above.

2 Jesus, the Saviour, this gospel to tell,
   joyfully came;
   came with the helpless and hopeless to dwell,
   sharing their sorrow and shame;
   seeking the lost,
   saving, redeeming at measureless cost.

3 Jesus is seeking the wanderers yet;
   Why do they roam?
   Love only waits to forgive and forget;
   Home! weary wanderers, home!
   Wonderful love
   dwells in the heart of the Father above.

4 Come to my heart, O Thou wonderful love,
   come and abide,
   lifting my life till it rises above
   envy and falsehood and pride;
   seeking to be
   lowly and humble, a learner of Thee.

95   Come let us sing

Words and music: Ruth Hooke

96 Come let us worship

I AM THE BREAD OF LIFE

Words: after S Suzanne Toolan
Michael Baughan
Music: Suzanne Toolan
arranged Christian Strover

Come, let us wor-ship Christ to the glo-ry of God the Fa-ther, for He is wor-thy of all our love; He died and rose for us! praise Him as Lord and Sav-iour. *And when the trum-pet shall sound, and Je-sus comes in great power,___ then He will raise us to be with Him for ev-er-more.*

1   Come, let us worship Christ
    to the glory of God the Father,
    for He is worthy of all our love;
    He died and rose for us!
    praise Him as Lord and Saviour.
       And when the trumpet shall sound,
       and Jesus comes in great power,
       then He will raise us to be with Him
       for evermore.

2   'I am the Bread of Life;
    he who comes to Me shall not hunger:
    and all who trust in Me shall not thirst' –
    this is what Jesus said:
    praise Him as Lord and Saviour.
       And when the trumpet . . .

3   'I am the door to life;
    he who enters by Me is saved,
    abundant life he will then receive' –
    this is what Jesus said:
    praise Him as Lord and Saviour.
       And when the trumpet . . .

4   'I am the Light of the world;
    if you follow Me, darkness ceases,
    and in its place comes the light of life' –
    this is what Jesus said:
    praise Him as Lord and Saviour.
       And when the trumpet . . .

5   Lord, we are one with You;
    we rejoice in Your new creation:
    our hearts are fired by Your saving love –
    take up our lives, O Lord,
    and use us for Your glory.
       And when the trumpet . . .

97 # Come, let us worship

Words: from Psalm 95
Sarah Turner-Smith
Music: Paul Herrington
arranged Phil Burt

Come, let us wor-ship our Re - deem — er, let us bow down be-fore His throne; ___ come, let us kneel be-fore our Ma — ker: ho - ly is His name. ___

1 Come in - to His pre-sence with thanks-
2   We are the peo - ple of His
3   All prais-es be to God the

98
Come now with awe

FINLANDIA   11 10 11 10 11 10

Words: Timothy Dudley-Smith
Music: J Sibelius (1865–1957)

Come now with awe, earth's an-cient vi-gil keep-ing:

cold un-der star - light lies the sto-ny way.

Down from the hill - side see the shep-herds creep-ing,

hear in our hearts the whis-pered news they say:

'Laid in a man-ger lies an in-fant sleep-ing,

Christ our Re-deem-er, born for us to-day.'

1 Come now with awe, earth's ancient vigil keeping:
  cold under starlight lies the stony way.
  Down from the hillside see the shepherds creeping,
  hear in our hearts the whispered news they say:
  'Laid in a manger lies an infant sleeping,
  Christ our Redeemer, born for us today.'

2 Come now with joy to worship and adore Him;
  hushed in the stillness, wonder and behold –
  Christ in the stable where His mother bore Him,
  Christ whom the prophets faithfully foretold:
  High King of ages, low we kneel before Him,
  starlight for silver, lantern-light for gold.

3 Come now with faith, the age-long secret guessing,
  hearts rapt in wonder, soul and spirit stirred –
  see in our likeness love beyond expressing,
  All God has spoken, all the prophets heard;
  born for us sinners, bearer of all blessing,
  Flesh of our flesh, behold the eternal Word!

4 Come now with love: beyond our comprehending
  Love in its fulness lies in mortal span!
  How should we love, whom Love is so befriending?
  Love rich in mercy since our race began
  now stoops to save us, sighs and sorrows ending,
  Jesus our Saviour, Son of God made man.

99 Come on and celebrate

Words and music: Patricia Morgan
Music arranged David Peacock

Lively

Come on and ce-le-brate! His gift of love we will

ce-le-brate – the Son of God, who loved_ us_____

_ and gave us life._____ We'll shout Your

praise, O King: You give us joy no-thing else can bring;

100   Come see the beauty of the Lord

Words and music: Graham Kendrick
Music arranged Christopher Norton

101   Come sing the praise of Jesus

Words: J C Winslow (1882–1974)
Music: American traditional melody
arranged D J Langford

Come sing the praise of Je-sus, sing His love with hearts a-flame, sing His won-drous birth of Ma-ry, when to save the world He came; tell the life He lived for oth-ers, and His migh-ty deeds pro-claim, for Je-sus Christ is King. *Praise and glo-ry be to Je - sus,*

praise and glo-ry be to Je - sus, praise and glo-ry be to

Je - sus, for Je - sus Christ is King!

1 Come sing the praise of Jesus,
　sing His love with hearts aflame,
　sing His wondrous birth of Mary,
　when to save the world He came;
　tell the life He lived for others,
　and His mighty deeds proclaim,
　for Jesus Christ is King.
　　Praise and glory be to Jesus,
　　praise and glory be to Jesus,
　　praise and glory be to Jesus,
　　for Jesus Christ is King!

2 When foes arose and slew Him,
　He was victor in the fight;
　over death and hell He triumphed
　in His resurrection-might;
　He has raised our fallen manhood
　and enthroned it in the height,
　for Jesus Christ is King.
　　Praise and glory . . .

3 There's joy for all who serve Him,
　more than human tongue can say;
　there is pardon for the sinner,
　and the night is turned to day;
　there is healing for our sorrows,
　there is music all the way,
　for Jesus Christ is King.
　　Praise and glory . . .

4 We witness to His beauty,
　and we spread His love abroad;
　and we cleave the host of darkness,
　with the Spirit's piercing sword;
　we will lead the souls in prison
　to the freedom of the Lord,
　for Jesus Christ is King.
　　Praise and glory . . .

5 To Jesus be the glory,
　the dominion, and the praise;
　He is Lord of all creation,
　He is guide of all our ways;
　and the world shall be His empire
　in the fulness of the days,
　for Jesus Christ is King.
　　Praise and glory . . .

102   Come, thou long-expected Jesus

STUTTGART   87 87

Words: Charles Wesley (1707–88)
Music: melody by C F Witt (1660–1716)

Come, Thou long-ex-pect-ed Je-sus, born to set Thy peo-ple free;

from our fears and sins re-lease us; let us_ find_ our_ rest in Thee.

1 Come, Thou long-expected Jesus,
  born to set Thy people free;
  from our fears and sins release us;
  let us find our rest in Thee.

2 Israel's strength and consolation,
  hope of all the earth Thou art;
  dear desire of every nation,
  joy of every longing heart.

3 Born Thy people to deliver;
  born a child, and yet a King;
  born to reign in us for ever;
  now Thy gracious kingdom bring.

4 By Thine own eternal Spirit
  rule in all our hearts alone:
  by Thine all-sufficient merit
  raise us to Thy glorious throne.

103 Come, ye faithful

NEANDER   87 87 87

Words: Job Hupton (1762–1849)
and J M Neale (1818–66)
Music: from Chorale *Unser Herrscher*
by J Neander (1650–80)

Come, ye faith-ful, raise the an-them, cleave the_ skies with shouts of praise;

sing to Him who found the ran-som, An-cient of e - ter-nal days,

God e-ter-nal, Word in-car-nate, whom the heaven of heaven o-beys.

1 Come, ye faithful, raise the anthem,
cleave the skies with shouts of praise;
sing to Him who found the ransom,
Ancient of eternal days,
God eternal, Word incarnate,
whom the heaven of heaven obeys.

2 Ere He raised the lofty mountains,
formed the sea, or built the sky,
love eternal, free, and boundless,
forced the Lord of life to die,
lifted up the Prince of princes
on the throne of Calvary.

3 Now on those eternal mountains
stands the sapphire throne, all bright,
with the ceaseless alleluias
which they raise, the sons of light;
Sion's people tell His praises,
victor after hard-won fight.

4 Laud and honour to the Father,
laud and honour to the Son,
laud and honour to the Spirit,
ever Three and ever One,
One in love, and One in splendour,
while unending ages run.

104 Come to the waters

Words and music: Jodi Page Clark

With a gentle swing

Come___ to the wa - ters___ and I will give you rest;

___ come___ to the wa - ters___ and

you will be___ re - freshed.___

last time *Fine*

1 Je - sus said,_____ 'Come un - to
2 Je - sus said,_____ of the wa - ters
3 Je - sus said,_____ 'He_ who be -
4 So with joy_____ we_ shall draw

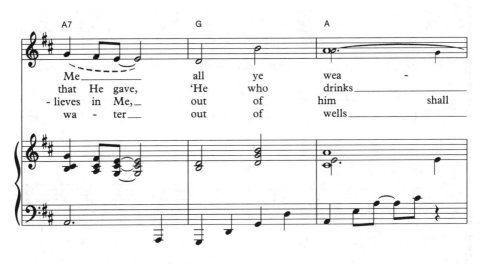

Me_____ all ye wea -
that He gave, 'He who drinks_____
- lieves in Me,_ out of him shall
wa - ter_ out of wells_____

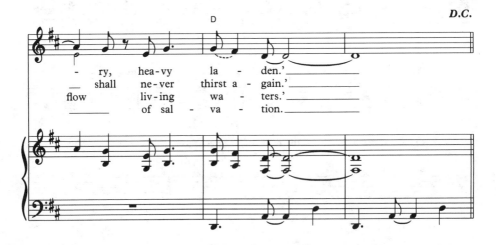

- ry, hea - vy la - den.'_____
_ shall ne - ver thirst a - gain.'_____
flow liv - ing wa - ters.'_____
_____ of sal - va - tion._____

Come, watch with us

Words: Timothy Dudley-Smith
Music: Phil Burt

Come, watch with us this Christ-mas night; our hearts must tra - vel far to dark - ened hills and hea - vens bright with star on shin - ing star; to where in sha - dowy si - lence sleep the fields of Beth - le - hem, as shep-herds

wake their watch to keep and we will watch____ with them.

1 Come, watch with us this Christmas night;
   our hearts must travel far
   to darkened hills and heavens bright
   with star on shining star;
   to where in shadowy silence sleep
       the fields of Bethlehem,
   as shepherds wake their watch to keep
   and we will watch with them.

2 Who would not join the angel songs
   that tell the Saviour's birth?
   The Lord for whom creation longs
   has come at last to earth;
   the fulness of the Father's love
       is ours at Bethlehem,
   while angels throng the skies above
   and we will sing with them.

3 Who would not journey far to share
   the wisdom of the wise,
   and gaze with them in wonder where
   the world's Redeemer lies?
   The Lord of all the lords that are
       is born at Bethlehem,
   and kings shall kneel beneath His star
   and we will bow with them.

4 Lift every heart the hymn of praise
   that all creation sings;
   the angel host its homage pays,
   the shepherds and the kings.
   For earth and sky with one accord,
       O Child of Bethlehem,
   are come to worship Christ the Lord
   and we will come with them.

106 Come, you thankful people, come

ST GEORGE'S, WINDSOR   77 77 D

Words: H Alford (1810–71)
in this version Jubilate Hymns
Music: C J Elvey (1816–93)

Come, you thank-ful peo-ple, come, raise the song of har-vest home!

fruit and crops are gath-ered in safe be-fore the storms be-gin:

God our ma-ker will pro-vide for our needs to be sup-plied;

come, with all His peo-ple, come, raise the song of har-vest home!

1   Come, you thankful people, come,
raise the song of harvest home!
fruit and crops are gathered in
safe before the storms begin:
God our maker will provide
for our needs to be supplied;
come, with all His people, come,
raise the song of harvest home!

2   All the world is God's own field,
harvests for His praise to yield;
wheat and weeds together sown
here for joy or sorrow grown:
first the blade and then the ear,
then the full corn shall appear –
Lord of harvest, grant that we
wholesome grain and pure may be.

3   For the Lord our God shall come
and shall bring His harvest home;
He Himself on that great day,
worthless things shall take away,
give His angels charge at last
in the fire the weeds to cast,
but the fruitful ears to store
in His care for evermore.

4   Even so, Lord, quickly come –
bring Your final harvest home!
gather all Your people in
free from sorrow, free from sin,
there together purified,
ever thankful at Your side –
come, with all Your angels, come,
bring that glorious harvest home!

107(i) Cradled in a manger

PLEADING SAVIOUR (SALTASH)   87 87 D

Words: George Stringer Rowe (1830–1913)
Music: melody from *Plymouth Collection*, USA, 1855
arranged R Vaughan Williams (1872–1958)

Crad-led_ in a_ man-ger, mean-ly laid the_ Son of_ Man His head;

sleep-ing_ His first earth-ly slum-ber where the_ ox-en_ had been fed.

Hap-py_ were those shep-herds listen-ing to the_ ho-ly an-gel's word;

hap-py_ they with-in that sta-ble, wor-ship-ping their in-fant Lord.

1   Cradled in a manger, meanly
        laid the Son of Man His head;
    sleeping His first earthly slumber
        where the oxen had been fed.
    Happy were those shepherds listening
        to the holy angel's word;
    happy they within that stable,
        worshipping their infant Lord.

2   Happy all who hear the message
        of His coming from above;
    happier still who hail His coming,
        and with praises greet His love.
    Blessèd Saviour, Christ most holy,
        in a manger thou didst rest;
    canst Thou stoop again, yet lower
        and abide within my breast?

3   Evil things are there before Thee;
        in the heart, where they have fed,
    wilt Thou pitifully enter,
        Son of Man, and lay Thy head?
    Enter, then, O Christ most holy;
        make a Christmas in my heart;
    make a heaven on my manger:
        It is heaven where Thou art.

4   And to those who never listened
        to the message of Thy birth,
    who have winter, but no Christmas
        bringing them Thy peace on earth,
    send to these the joyful tidings;
        by all people, in each home,
    be there heard the Christmas anthem:
        Praise to God, the Christ has come!

107(ii) Cradled in a manger

ST WINIFRED   87 87 D

Words: George Stringer Rowe (1830–1913)
Music: S J P Dunman (1843–1913)

Crad-led in a man-ger, mean-ly laid the Son of Man His head;

sleep-ing His first earth-ly slum-ber where the ox - en had been fed.

Hap-py were those shep-herds listen-ing to the ho - ly an-gel's word;

hap-py they with-in that sta - ble, wor-ship-ping their in-fant Lord.

1 Cradled in a manger, meanly
    laid the Son of Man His head;
sleeping His first earthly slumber
    where the oxen had been fed.
Happy were those shepherds listening
    to the holy angel's word;
happy they within that stable,
    worshipping their infant Lord.

2 Happy all who hear the message
    of His coming from above;
happier still who hail His coming,
    and with praises greet His love.
Blessèd Saviour, Christ most holy,
    in a manger thou didst rest;
canst Thou stoop again, yet lower
    and abide within my breast?

3 Evil things are there before Thee;
    in the heart, where they have fed,
wilt Thou pitifully enter,
    Son of Man, and lay Thy head?
Enter, then, O Christ most holy;
    make a Christmas in my heart;
make a heaven on my manger:
    It is heaven where Thou art.

4 And to those who never listened
    to the message of Thy birth,
who have winter, but no Christmas
    bringing them Thy peace on earth,
send to these the joyful tidings;
    by all people, in each home,
be there heard the Christmas anthem:
    Praise to God, the Christ has come!

108   Create in me

Words and music: Dave Fellingham
Music arranged Roland Fudge

Wash me, cleanse me, pu - ri - fy me,

make my heart as white as snow.

Cre - ate in me a clean heart, O___ God, and re -

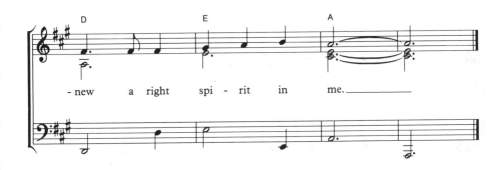

- new a right spi - rit in me.___

109   Crown Him with many crowns

DIADEMATA   DSM

Words: Matthew Bridges (1800–94)
and Godfrey Thring (1823–1903)
Music: George Elvey (1816–93)

Crown Him with ma - ny crowns, the Lamb up - on His

throne; Hark! how the heaven - ly an - them drowns all

mu - sic but its___ own: a - wake, my soul, and

sing of Him who died for thee, and

hail Him as thy cho-sen King through all e - ter - ni - ty.

1 Crown Him with many crowns,
   the Lamb upon His throne;
   Hark! how the heavenly anthem drowns
   all music but its own:
   awake, my soul, and sing
   of Him who died for thee,
   and hail Him as thy chosen King
   through all eternity.

2 Crown Him the Son of God
   before the worlds began;
   and ye who tread where He hath trod,
   crown Him the Son of Man,
   who every grief hath known
   that wrings the human breast,
   and takes and bears them for His own,
   that all in Him may rest.

3 Crown Him the Lord of life,
   who triumphed o'er the grave,
   and rose victorious in the strife,
   for those He came to save:
   His glories now we sing,
   who died and rose on high,
   who died eternal life to bring,
   and lives that death may die.

4 Crown Him the Lord of heaven,
   enthroned in worlds above;
   crown Him the King to whom is given
   the wondrous name of love:
   all hail, Redeemer, hail!
   for Thou hast died for me;
   Thy praise shall never, never fail
   throughout eternity.

110 Darkness like a shroud

ARISE, SHINE

Words and music: Graham Kendrick

Subdued, becoming bright

Capo 4(C)

1 Dark - ness like a shroud co - vers the earth,
2 Child - ren of the light, be clean and pure;
3 Here a - mong us now, Christ the Light
4 Like a ci - ty bright, so let us blaze;

e - vil like a cloud co - vers the peo-ple; but the
rise, you sleep - ers, Christ will shine on you: take the
kin - dles bright-er flames in our trem-bling hearts: Liv-ing
lights in ev - ery street turn - ing night to day: and the

Lord will rise up - on you, and His glo - ry will ap -
Spi - rit's flash - ing two-edged sword and with faith de - clare God's
Word, our lamp, come guide our feet – as we walk as one in
dark - ness shall not ov - er - come, till the ful - ness of Christ's

- pear on you, na - tions will come to your
migh - ty word; stand up, and in His strength be
light and peace, jus - tice and truth shine like the
king - dom comes, dawn - ing to God's e - ter - nal

111 Dear Lord and Father of mankind

REPTON   86 88 6 extended

Words: John Greenleaf Whittier (1807–82)
Music: C Hubert H Parry (1848–1918)

Dear Lord and Fa-ther___ of man-kind, for-give our fool-ish ways; re-clothe us in our right-ful mind; in pur-er lives Thy ser-vice___ find, in___ deep-er rev-erence, praise, in deep-er rev-erence praise.

1 Dear Lord and Father of mankind,
   forgive our foolish ways;
   re-clothe us in our rightful mind;
   in purer lives Thy service find,
   in deeper reverence, praise.

2 In simple trust like theirs who heard,
   beside the Syrian sea,
   the gracious calling of the Lord,
   let us, like them, without a word
   rise up and follow Thee.

3 O Sabbath rest by Galilee!
   O calm of hills above,
   where Jesus knelt to share with Thee
   the silence of eternity,
   interpreted by love!

4 Drop Thy still dews of quietness,
   till all our strivings cease;
   take from our souls the strain and stress,
   and let our ordered lives confess
   the beauty of Thy peace.

5 Breathe through the heats of our desire
   Thy coolness and Thy balm;
   let sense be dumb, let flesh retire;
   speak through the earthquake, wind, and fire,
   O still small voice of calm!

112 Delight yourself in the Lord

Words and music: Andy Silver

De - light your - self in the Lord,_____ and He will give you the de - sires_ of your heart. Com - mit your way to the Lord;_____ trust in Him and He will make your right-eous-ness shine, _ shin-ing like the dawn and like the noon-day sun.

113   Delight yourselves in the Lord

Words and music: David Bolton

De - light your-selves in the Lord,_____ de - light your-selves in the

Lord;_____ for He de-lights in the prais - es of His

own peo - - ple;_____ for He de-lights in the

prais - es of His own peo - - ple.

Let your well spring up with-in and o - ver-flow to

one an - oth - er; let your well spring up with-in and

o - ver-flow to the Lord.

Delight yourselves in the Lord,
delight yourselves in the Lord;
for He delights in the praises
of His own people;
for He delights in the praises
of His own people.

Let your well spring up within
and overflow to one another;
let your well spring up within
and overflow to the Lord.

114   Ding dong! Merrily on high

BRANLE DE L'OFFICIAL

Words: George Ratcliffe Woodward (1848–1934)
Music: 16th-cent. French melody
arranged Charles Wood and B V Burnett

1 Ding dong! Mer-ri-ly on high   in heaven the bells are ring-ing.
2 E'en so, here be-low, be-low,   let steep-le bells be swung-en;
3 Pray you, du-ti-ful-ly prime your ma-tin chime, ye ring-ers;

Ding dong! Ve-ri-ly the sky   is riven with an-gels sing-ing:
and i-o, i-o, i-o,   by priest and peo-ple sung-en!
may you beau-ti-ful-ly rime your eve-time song, ye sing-ers:

Glo — — — — — — — — — — — — — — — — — *ri-a, ho-san-na in ex-cel-sis!*

115   Do not be afraid

Words and music: Gerald Markland
Music arranged Roland Fudge

With warmth

Do not be a - fraid,_____ for I have re -

- deemed you._____ I have called you by your name;_____ you are

Mine._____

1 When you walk through the wa - ters I'll be
2 When the fire is____ burn - ing all a -
3 When the fear of____ lone - li - ness is
4 When you dwell in the ex - ile of the
5 You are Mine, O My child; I am your

with you; you will ne - ver sink be - neath_ the__ waves.
- round you, you will ne - ver be con - sumed by the flames.
loom - ing, then re - mem - ber I am at____ your__ side.
stran - ger, re - mem - ber you are pre - cious in My eyes.
Fa - ther, and I love you with a per - fect__ love.

116   Down from His glory

O SOLE MIO   11 12 11 10 with refrain

Words: William E Booth-Clibborn (1893–1969)
Music: Eduardo di Capun
arranged Norman Johnson

Down from His glo-ry, ev-er-liv-ing sto-ry, my God and Sav-iour came, and Je-sus was His name; born in a man-ger to His own a stran-ger, a man of sor-rows, tears and a - go-ny! O how I love Him! how I a - dore Him! My breath, my

sun-shine, my all-in - all! ___ The great Cre - a - tor _____ be-came my

Sav - iour, and all God's ful - ness _____ dwell-eth in Him!

1 Down from His glory, ever-living story,
   my God and Saviour came, and Jesus was His name;
   born in a manger to His own a stranger,
   a man of sorrows, tears and agony!
       O how I love Him! how I adore Him!
       My breath, my sunshine, my all-in-all!
       The great Creator became my Saviour,
       and all God's fulness dwelleth in Him!

2 What condescension, bringing us redemption,
   that in the dead of night, not one faint hope in sight;
   God gracious, tender, laid aside His splendour,
   stooping to woo, to win, to save my soul.
       O how I love Him . . .

3 Without reluctance, flesh and blood, His substance,
   He took the form of man, revealed the hidden plan;
   O glorious mystery, sacrifice of Calvary!
   And now I know He is the great 'I AM'!
       O how I love Him . . .

117   Do not be worried and upset

Words: from John 14: 1–6
Music: G Taylor

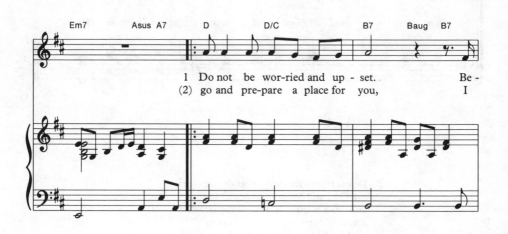

1 Do not be wor-ried and up - set.   Be -
(2) go and pre-pare a place for you,   I

- lieve in God, be-lieve al - so in   Me,
will come back and take you to My - self,

118 Draw near to God

Achor

Words and music: © 1980 Springtide/Word Music (UK), (a division of Word (UK) Ltd)
9 Holdom Avenue, Bletchley, Milton Keynes MK1 1QR, UK

119 El-Shaddai

Words: Michael Card
Music: John Thompson

We will praise___ and lift You high,___ El - Sha - ddai.

1–4.

last time

1 Through your love ___

El-Shaddai, El-Shaddai
  (God Almighty, God Almighty)
El-Elyon na Adonai
  (God in the highest, Oh Lord)
Age to age You're still the same
by the power of the name.
El-Shaddai, El-Shaddai
  (God Almighty, God Almighty)
Erkamka na Adonai
  (We will love You, Oh Lord)
We will praise and lift You high,
El-Shaddai.

1 Through Your love and through the ram
   You saved the son of Abraham.
   Through the power of Your hand,
   turned the sea into dry land.
   To the outcast on her knees
   You were the God who really sees,
   and by Your might You set Your children free.
      El-Shaddai, El-Shaddai . . .

2 Through the years You made it clear,
   that the time of Christ was near.
   Though the people couldn't see
   what Messiah ought to be.
   Though Your word contained the plan
   they just could not understand.
   Your most awesome work was done
   through the frailty of Your Son.
      El-Shaddai, El-Shaddai . . .

120 Emmanuel

Words: Greg Leavers
Music: Greg Leavers and Phil Burt

Lord of lords   **ALL is** He.
Lord of lords

God Him-self_ will give a sign; a vir-gin shall bear a son who shall be

called Em - ma - nu - el._____

Emmanuel, (Emmanuel,)
God with us, (God with us,)
Wonderful (Wonderful)
Counsellor, (Counsellor,)
Prince of Peace –
a Saviour is born to redeem the world,
and His name is Jesus.
King of kings, (King of kings,)
Lord of lords (Lord of lords)
is He.

1   God Himself will give a sign;
    a virgin shall bear a son
    who shall be called Emmanuel.
    Emmanuel . . .

2   People who now walk in darkness
    soon will see the light of Jesus,
    He is the light of the world.
    Emmanuel . . .

3   Hear a voice cry in the desert,
    clear a way for the Messiah,
    make straight a highway for God.
    Emmanuel . . .

4   Bringing good news, healing heartaches,
    preaching freedom, releasing captives,
    giving a mantle of praise.
    Emmanuel . . .

121 Emmanuel, Emmanuel

Words and music: Bob McGee

With warmth

Em-man-u-el,_____ Em-man-u-el,_____

His name is called_____ Em-man-u-el =

God with us,_____ re-vealed in us =

His name is called_____ Em-man-u-el.

122   Eternal Father, strong to save

MELITA   88 88 88

Words: William Whiting (1825–78)
Music: John Bacchus Dykes (1823–76)

E - ter-nal Fa-ther, strong to save, whose arm hath bound the_ rest-less wave, who bidd'st the migh-ty o - cean deep its own ap - point-ed lim - its keep: O hear us when we cry to Thee for those in per - il on the sea.

1 Eternal Father, strong to save,
  whose arm hath bound the restless wave,
  who bidd'st the mighty ocean deep
  its own appointed limits keep:
  O hear us when we cry to Thee
  for those in peril on the sea.

2 O Christ, whose voice the waters heard,
  and hushed their raging at Thy word,
  who walkedst on the foaming deep,
  and calm amid the storm didst sleep:
  O hear us when we cry to Thee
  for those in peril on the sea.

3 O Holy Spirit, who didst brood
  upon the waters dark and rude,
  and bid their angry tumult cease,
  and give, for wild confusion, peace:
  O hear us when we cry to Thee
  for those in peril on the sea.

4 O Trinity of love and power,
  our brethren shield in danger's hour;
  from rock and tempest, fire and foe,
  protect them wheresoe'er they go:
  thus evermore shall rise to Thee
  glad hymns of praise from land and sea.

123   Eternal God

Words and music: Dave Fellingham
Music arranged Roland Fudge

E - ter - nal God, we come to You, we come be - fore Your throne; we en - ter by a new and liv-ing way, with con - fi - dence we come.

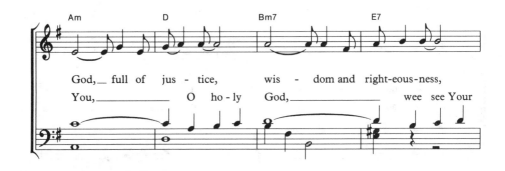

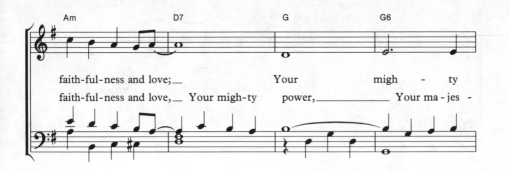

faith-ful-ness and love;___ Your migh - ty
faith-ful-ness and love,___ Your migh-ty power,_____ Your ma - jes-

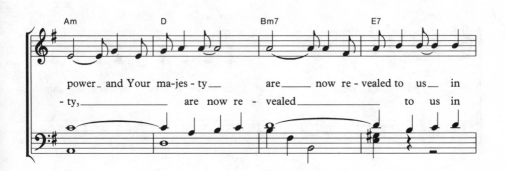

power___ and Your ma-jes - ty___ are___ now re - vealed to us___ in
- ty,_____ are now re - vealed_____ to us in

Je - sus who has died___ for our sin, Je - sus who was raised from the dead,
Je - sus who has died,___ Je - sus who was raised,

Je - sus now ex - alt - ed on___ high._____
Je - sus now ex - alt - ed on high._____

Eternal God, we come to You,
we come before Your throne;
we enter by a new and living way,
with confidence we come.
We declare Your faithfulness,
Your promises are true;
we will now draw near to worship You.

MEN
O holy God, we come to You,
O holy God, wee see Your faithfulness and love,
Your mighty power, Your majesty,
are now revealed to us in Jesus who has died,
Jesus who was raised,
Jesus now exalted on high.

WOMEN
O holy God, full of justice,
wisdom and righteousness,
faithfulness and love;
Your mighty power and Your majesty
are now revealed to us
in Jesus who has died for our sin,
Jesus who was raised from the dead,
Jesus now exalted on high.

124   Exalt the Lord our God

Words and music: Rick Ridings
Music arranged Roland Fudge

125 Faithful vigil ended

FAITHFUL VIGIL   65 65

Words: from Luke 2
Timothy Dudley-Smith
Music: David Wilson

Faith-ful vi-gil end-ed, watch-ing, wait-ing cease:—

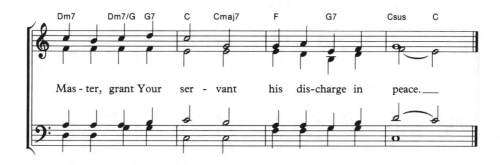

Mas-ter, grant Your ser-vant his dis-charge in peace.—

1 Faithful vigil ended,
watching, waiting cease:
Master, grant Your servant
his discharge in peace.

2 All the Spirit promised,
all the Father willed,
now these eyes behold it
perfectly fulfilled.

3 This Your great deliverance
sets Your people free;
Christ their light uplifted
all the nations see.

4 Christ, Your people's glory!
Watching, doubting cease:
grant to us Your servants
our discharge in peace.

126 Facing a task unfinished

Aurelia 76 76 D

Words: Frank Houghton (1894–1972)
Music: Samuel Sebastian Wesley (1810–76)

Fac - ing a task un - fin - ished, that drives us to our knees,

a need that, un - dim - in - ished, re - bukes our sloth-ful ease.

We who re - joice to know Thee, re - new be-fore Thy throne

the sol-emn pledge we owe Thee, to go and make Thee known.

1 Facing a task unfinished,
  that drives us to our knees,
  a need that, undiminished,
  rebukes our slothful ease.
  We who rejoice to know Thee,
  renew before Thy throne
  the solemn pledge we owe Thee,
  to go and make Thee known.

2 Where other lords beside Thee
  hold their unhindered sway,
  where forces that defied Thee
  defy Thee still today.
  With none to heed their crying
  for life, and love, and light,
  unnumbered souls are dying,
  and pass into the night.

3 We bear the torch that, flaming,
  fell from the hands of those
  who gave their lives, proclaiming
  that Jesus died and rose.
  Ours is the same commission,
  the same glad message ours,
  fired by the same ambition,
  to Thee we yield our powers.

4 O Father who sustained them,
  O Spirit who inspired,
  Saviour, whose love constrained them
  to toil with zeal untired.
  From cowardice defend us,
  from lethargy awake!
  Forth on Thine errands send us,
  to labour for Thy sake.

127 Father, although I cannot see

MORDEN   86 86 86

Words: John Eddison
Music: Norman Warren

Fa - ther, al - though I can - not see the fu - ture You_ have planned,___ and though the path is some - times dark and hard_ to un - der - stand:_____ yet give me faith, through joy and pain, to trace_ Your lov - ing

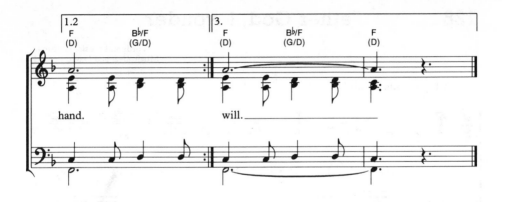

hand.

will._____

1 Father, although I cannot see
   the future You have planned,
   and though the path is sometimes dark
   and hard to understand:
   yet give me faith, through joy and pain,
   to trace Your loving hand.

2 When I recall that in the past
   Your promises have stood
   through each perplexing circumstance
   and every changing mood,
   I rest content that all things work
   together for my good.

3 Whatever, then, the future brings
   of good or seeming ill,
   I ask for strength to follow You
   and grace to trust You still;
   and I would look for no reward,
   except to do Your will.

128 Father God, I wonder

Words and music: Ian Smale
Music arranged David Peacock

Lively Spanish style

Fa - ther God, I won - der how I man-aged to ex -

- ist with - out the know-ledge of Your par - ent - hood

and Your lov-ing care. But now I am Your son, I am a -

-dopt-ed in Your fam - i - ly, and I can ne - ver

129 Father God, I love You

Words and music: Joan Robinson

Gently

1 Fa - ther God,_____ I love__ You,
2 Je - sus,_____ I love__ You,
3 Spi - rit,_____ I love__ You,
4 Al - le - lu - ia,

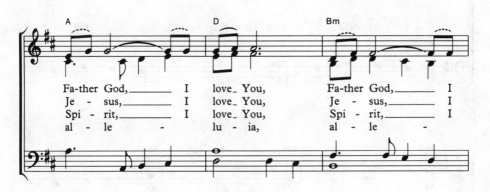

Fa - ther God,_____ I love_ You, Fa - ther God,_____ I
Je - sus,_____ I love_ You, Je - sus,_____ I
Spi - rit,_____ I love_ You, Spi - rit,_____ I
al - le - lu - ia, al - le -

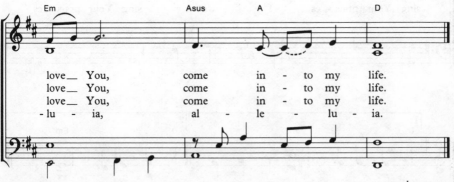

love__ You, come in - to my life.
love__ You, come in - to my life.
love__ You, come in - to my life.
-lu - ia, al - le - lu - ia.

repeat last verse

130 Father God, the Lord, Creator

WALTHAM 87 87

Words: John Richards
Music: H Albert (1604–51)
harmony by J S Bach (1685–1750)

Fa-ther God, the Lord, Cre-a-tor, by whose hand we all are fed,

in Your mer-cy re-cre-ate us at the break-ing of the Bread.

1 Father God, the Lord, Creator,
  by whose hand we all are fed,
  in Your mercy recreate us
  at the breaking of the Bread.

2 Christ our Lord, be present with us,
  risen victorious from the dead!
  In Your mercy may we know You,
  in the breaking of the Bread.

3 Holy Spirit, God's empowering,
  by whose life the Church is led;
  in Your mercy, send us strengthened
  from the breaking of the Bread.

4 Father, Son, and Holy Spirit,
  hear our praises – sung and said.
  From our hearts comes our thanksgiving
  for the breaking of the Bread.

131 Father God, we worship You

Words and music: Graham Kendrick
Music arranged Christopher Norton

1 Father God, we worship You,
  make us part of all You do.
  As You move among us now
  we worship You.

2 Jesus King, we worship You,
  help us listen now to You.
  As You move among us now
  we worship You.

3 Spirit pure, we worship You,
  with Your fire our zeal renew.
  As You move among us now
  we worship You.

132 Father, hear the prayer we offer

SUSSEX 87 87

Words: Love Maria Willis (1824–1908)
Music: English traditional melody
adapted by R Vaughan Williams (1872–1958)

Fa-ther, hear the prayer we_ of-fer: not for ease that prayer shall be,

but for strength, that we may ev - er live our lives cour - age - ous - ly.

1 Father, hear the prayer we offer:
   not for ease that prayer shall be,
   but for strength, that we may ever
   live our lives courageously.

2 Not for ever in green pastures
   do we ask our way to be:
   but by steep and rugged pathways
   would we strive to climb to Thee.

3 Not for ever by still waters
   would we idly quiet stay;
   but would smite the living fountains
   from the rocks along our way.

4 Be our strength in hours of weakness,
   in our wanderings be our guide;
   through endeavour, failure, danger,
   Father, be Thou at our side.

5 Let our path be bright or dreary,
   storm or sunshine be our share;
   may our souls, in hope unweary,
   make Thy work our ceaseless prayer.

133 Father, I place into Your hands

Words and music: Jenny Hewer

Fa-ther, I place in - to Your hands the things that I can't do.

Fa-ther, I place in - to Your hands the times that I've been through.

Fa-ther, I place in - to Your hands the way that I should go, for I

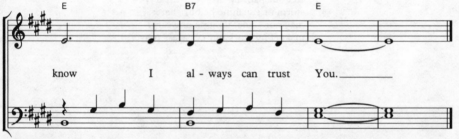

know I al - ways can trust You.

Words and music: © 1975 Thankyou Music,
PO Box 75, Eastbourne, East Sussex BN23 6NW, UK

1   Father, I place into Your hands
    the things that I can't do.
    Father, I place into Your hands
    the times that I've been through.
    Father, I place into Your hands
    the way that I should go,
    for I know I always can trust You.

2   Father, I place into Your hands
    my friends and my family.
    Father, I place into Your hands
    the things that trouble me.
    Father, I place into Your hands
    the person I would be,
    for I know I always can trust You.

3   Father, we love to seek Your face,
    we love to hear Your voice.
    Father, we love to sing Your praise,
    and in Your name rejoice.
    Father, we love to walk with You
    and in Your presence rest,
    for we know we always can trust You.

4   Father, I want to be with You
    and do the things You do.
    Father, I want to speak the words
    that You are speaking too.
    Father, I want to love the ones
    that You will draw to You,
    for I know that I am one with You.

134 Father in heaven

Words and music: Dave Bilbrough
Music arranged Christopher Norton

Fa-ther in hea-ven, our voi-ces we raise: re-ceive our de-vo-tion, re-ceive now our praise as we sing of the glo-ry__ of all that You've done – the great-est love-sto-ry that's ev-er been sung. *And we will*

1 Father in heaven,
   our voices we raise:
   receive our devotion,
   receive now our praise
   as we sing of the glory
   of all that You've done –
   the greatest love-story
   that's ever been sung.
   And we will crown You Lord of all,
   yes, we will crown You Lord of all,
   for You have won the victory:
   yes, we will crown You Lord of all.

2 Father in heaven,
   our lives are Your own;
   we've been caught by a vision
   of Jesus alone –
   who came as a servant
   to free us from sin:
   Father in heaven,
   our worship we bring.
   And we will crown . . .

3 We will sing Alleluia,
   we will sing to the King,
   to our mighty Deliverer
   our alleluias will ring.
   Yes, our praise is resounding
   to the Lamb on the throne:
   He alone is exalted
   through the love He has shown.
   And we will crown . . .

135 Father in heaven, how we love You

Words and music: Bob Fitts
Music arranged Christopher Norton

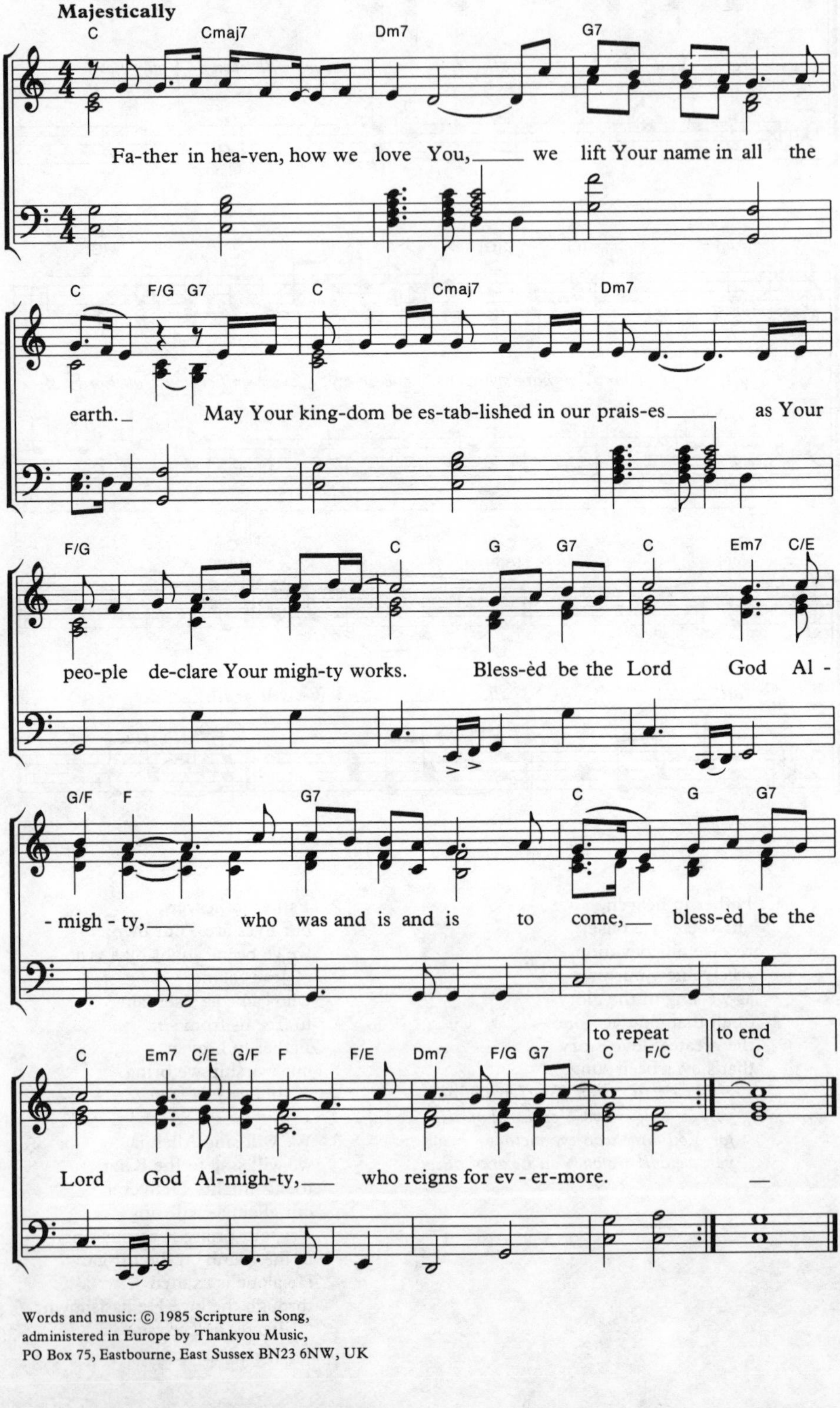

Majestically
C Cmaj7 Dm7 G7
Fa-ther in hea-ven, how we love You, we lift Your name in all the
C F/G G7 C Cmaj7 Dm7
earth. May Your king-dom be es-tab-lished in our prais-es as Your
F/G C G G7 C Em7 C/E
peo-ple de-clare Your migh-ty works. Bless-èd be the Lord God Al -
G/F F G7 C G G7
- migh - ty, who was and is and is to come, bless-èd be the
to repeat
to end
C Em7 C/E G/F F F/E Dm7 F/G G7 C F/C C
Lord God Al-migh-ty, who reigns for ev - er-more.

136 Father, sending Your anointed Son

ST ANDREW   87 87

Words: John Richards
Music: E H Thorne (1834–1916)

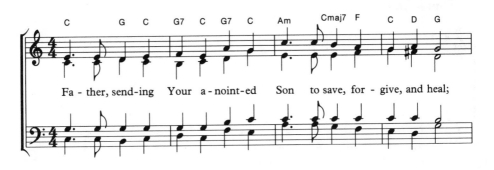

Fa - ther, send-ing Your a - noint-ed Son to save, for - give, and heal;

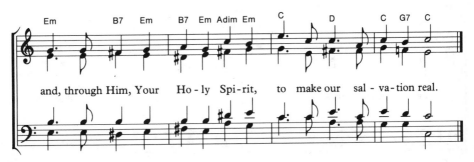

and, through Him, Your Ho - ly Spi-rit, to make our sal - va-tion real.

1 Father, sending Your anointed
   Son to save, forgive, and heal;
   and, through Him, Your Holy Spirit,
   to make our salvation real.

2 Look upon our ills and trouble,
   and on those who suffer much.
   Send Your church the Spirit's unction
   in Christ's name to heal and touch.

3 Grant forgiveness to the faithful;
   bring to unity their prayer;
   use it for Your work unhindered,
   through both sacrament and care.

OPTIONAL VERSE
FOR WHEN ANOINTING TAKES PLACE
4 May the *one/ones* to be anointed
   outwardly with oil this hour,
   know Christ's fullest restoration
   through the Holy Spirit's power.

5 Heal Your church! Anoint and send us
   out into the world to tell
   of Your love and blessings to us;
   how, in Christ, 'All will be well.'

137   Father make us one

Words and music: Rick Ridings
Music arranged Christopher Norton

Prayerfully

1 Fa - ther make us one,____ Fa - ther make us____ one,____ that the world may know Thou hast sent the Son,____ Fa - ther make us one. 2 Be -

- hold how plea - sant and how good it is_____ for

breth - ren to dwell in____ u - ni - ty,_____ for there the

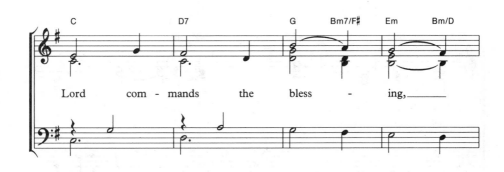

Lord com - mands the bless - ing,_____

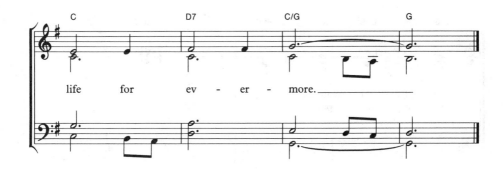

life for ev - er - more._____

138   Father, never was love so near

Words and music: Graham Kendrick
Music arranged Christopher Norton

1 Fa - ther,＿＿＿ ne - ver＿ was love so near; ten - der,＿＿＿ my deep - est wounds to heal.

2 Je - sus,＿＿＿ the heart of God re - vealed, with us,＿＿＿ feel - ing＿ the pain we feel.

Pre - cious__ to me,_____
Cut to__ the heart,_____

Your gift__ of
wound - ed__ for

love;   for me__ You
me,   tak - ing__ the

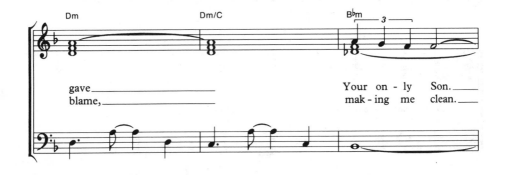

gave_____
blame,_____

Your on - ly Son.____
mak - ing me clean.____

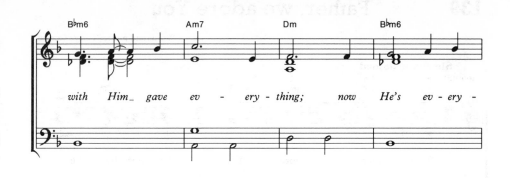

with Him   gave   ev –   ery - thing;   now   He's   ev – ery -

– thing   to   me.   me.

And   me.   now

He's   ev – ery - thing   to   me.

139   # Father, we adore You

Words and music: Terrye Coelho

This item may be sung as a 3-part round.

1 Father, we adore You,
  lay our lives before You:
  how we love You!

2 Jesus, we adore You,
  lay our lives before You:
  how we love You!

3 Spirit, we adore You,
  lay our lives before You:
  how we love You!

Words and music: © 1972 Maranatha! Music USA/Word Music (UK), (a division of Word (UK) Ltd)
9 Holdom Avenue, Bletchley, Milton Keynes MK1 1QR, UK
For British Isles, Republic of Ireland, Continent of Europe (Exc Benelux)

140

Father, we adore You

Words and music: Carl Tuttle
Music arranged Roland Fudge

1 Fa - ther, we a - dore You, You've drawn us to this place; we bow down be - fore_ You, hum - bly on our face.

2 Je - sus_ we_ love You, be - cause You first loved us; You reached out and healed us with Your migh - ty touch.

3 Spi - rit_ we_ need You, to lift us from this mire; con - sume and em - power us with Your ho - ly fire.

All the earth shall wor - ship at the throne of the

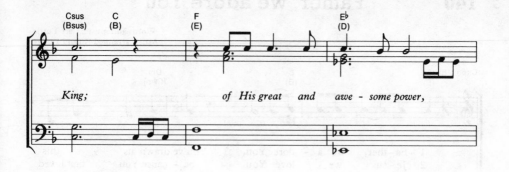

King;　　　　　　　　　of His great　and　awe - some power,

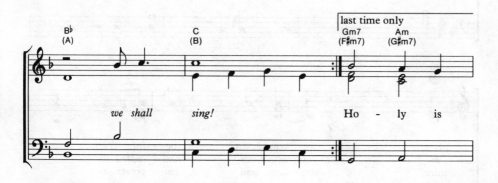

last time only

we shall　sing!　　　Ho - ly　is

He;　　　　　　　Bless - èd　is　He;

Wor - thy　is　He;　　　gra - cious　is

He; Faith - ful is He;

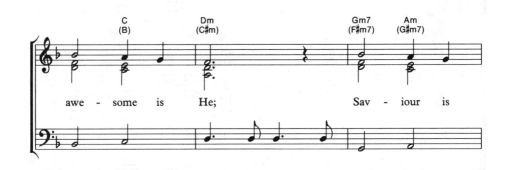

awe - some is He; Sav - iour is

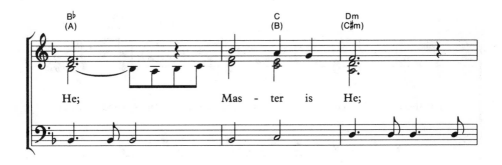

He; Mas - ter is He;

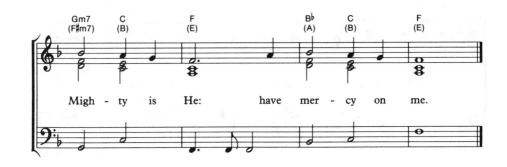

Migh - ty is He: have mer - cy on me.

141   Father, Your love is precious

Words and music: Everett Perry
Music arranged Roland Fudge

Fa - ther, Your love_ is pre - cious be - yond all loves,

Fa - ther,_ Your love o - ver - whelms me.____

Fa - ther, Your love_ is pre - cious be - yond all loves,

Fa - ther,_ Your love o - ver - whelms me.____ So I

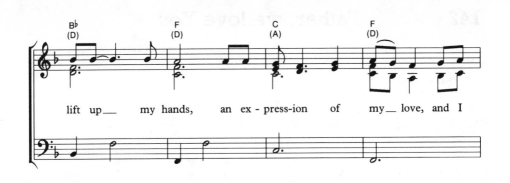

lift up___ my hands,   an ex - press-ion of   my___ love, and I

give You____ my heart   in   joy - ful   o - be - di-ence.

Fa - ther,   Your love___ is pre-cious   be - yond all loves,

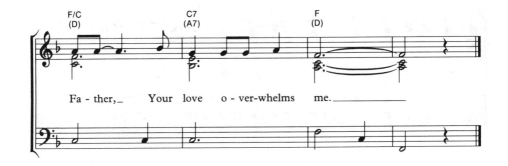

Fa - ther,_   Your love o - ver-whelms   me.____

142 Father, we love You

Words and music: Donna Adkins

Quite slow

1 Fa - ther, we love You, we wor - ship and a - dore You:
2 Je - sus, we love You, we wor - ship and a - dore You:
3 Spi - rit, we love You, we wor - ship and a - dore You:

glo - ri - fy Your name in all the earth.

Glo - ri - fy Your name, glo - ri - fy Your name,

glo - ri - fy Your name, in all the earth.

143 Fight the good fight

Duke Street   LM

Words: J S B Monsell (1811–75)
Music: John Hatton (d 1793)

Fight the good fight with all thy might;

Christ is thy strength, and Christ thy right. Lay hold on life, and

it shall be thy joy and crown e - ter - nal - ly.

1 Fight the good fight with all thy might;
   Christ is thy strength, and Christ thy right.
   Lay hold on life, and it shall be
   thy joy and crown eternally.

2 Run the straight race through God's good grace,
   lift up thine eyes, and seek His face;
   life with its path before thee lies;
   Christ is the way, and Christ the prize.

3 Cast care aside, lean on thy guide,
   His boundless mercy will provide;
   lean, and thy trusting soul shall prove
   Christ is thy life, and Christ thy love.

4 Faint not, nor fear, His arm is near,
   He changeth not, and thou art dear;
   only believe, and thou shalt see
   that Christ is all in all to thee.

144 Fear not, rejoice and be glad

Words and music: Priscilla Wright Porter

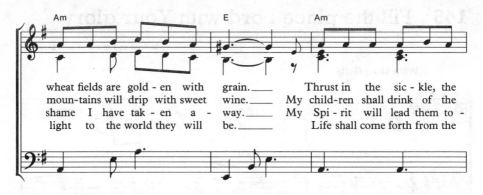

wheat fields are gold - en with grain.____ Thrust in the sic - kle, the
moun-tains will drip with sweet wine.____ My child-ren shall drink of the
shame I have tak - en a - way.____ My Spi - rit will lead them to -
light to the world they will be.____ Life shall come forth from the

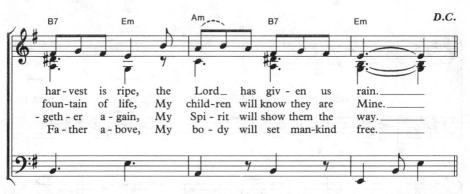

D.C.

har - vest is ripe, the Lord_ has giv - en us rain.____
foun-tain of life, My child-ren will know they are Mine.____
- geth - er a - gain, My Spi - rit will show them the way.____
Fa - ther a - bove, My bo - dy will set man-kind free.____

Fear not, rejoice and be glad,
the Lord hath done a great thing;
hath poured out His Spirit on all mankind,
on those who confess His name.

1 The fig tree is budding, the vine beareth fruit,
  the wheat fields are golden with grain.
  Thrust in the sickle, the harvest is ripe,
  the Lord has given us rain.
    Fear not, rejoice . . .

2 Ye shall eat in plenty and be satisfied,
  the mountains will drip with sweet wine.
  My children shall drink of the fountain of life,
  My children will know they are Mine.
    Fear not, rejoice . . .

3 My people shall know that I am the Lord,
  their shame I have taken away.
  My Spirit will lead them together again,
  My Spirit will show them the way.
    Fear not, rejoice . . .

4 My children shall dwell in a body of love,
  a light to the world they will be.
  Life shall come forth from the Father above,
  My body will set mankind free.
    Fear not, rejoice . . .

145 Fill the place Lord with Your glory

Words and music: Chris Bowater

we ex-alt You, we_____ a-dore You,_____ thank-ful

hearts now join_____ as one._____ You're the Christ,___ the

King___ of glo-ry,_____ Fa-ther's well____ be-lov - ed

Son._____ Fill the place, Lord, with Your glo-ry,_____

___ at this gath - ering of Your own._____

146(i)   Fill Thou my life

St Fulbert   CM

Words: Horatius Bonar (1808–82)
Music: H J Gauntlett (1805–76)

Fill Thou my life, O Lord my God, in ev-ery part with praise, that my whole be-ing may pro-claim Thy be-ing and Thy ways.

1   Fill Thou my life, O Lord my God,
    in every part with praise,
    that my whole being may proclaim
    Thy being and Thy ways.

2   Not for the lip of praise alone,
    nor e'en the praising heart,
    I ask, but for a life made up
    of praise in every part:

3   Praise in the common things of life,
    its goings out and in;
    praise in each duty and each deed,
    however small and mean.

4   Fill every part of me with praise:
    let all my being speak
    of Thee and of Thy love, O Lord,
    poor though I be and weak.

5   So shalt Thou, Lord, from me, e'en me,
    receive Thy glory due;
    and so shall I begin on earth
    the song for ever new.

6   So shall no part of day or night
    from sacredness be free;
    but all my life, in every step,
    be fellowship with Thee.

146(ii)   Fill Thou my life

RICHMOND   CM

Words: Horatius Bonar (1808–82)
Music: melody by Thomas Haweis (1734–1820)
arranged S Webbe the younger (c1770–1843)

1   Fill Thou my life, O Lord my God,
    in every part with praise,
    that my whole being may proclaim
    Thy being and Thy ways.

2   Not for the lip of praise alone,
    nor e'en the praising heart,
    I ask, but for a life made up
    of praise in every part:

3   Praise in the common things of life,
    its goings out and in;
    praise in each duty and each deed,
    however small and mean.

4   Fill every part of me with praise:
    let all my being speak
    of Thee and of Thy love, O Lord,
    poor though I be and weak.

5   So shalt Thou, Lord, from me, e'en me,
    receive Thy glory due;
    and so shall I begin on earth
    the song for ever new.

6   So shall no part of day or night
    from sacredness be free;
    but all my life, in every step,
    be fellowship with Thee.

147   Fill your hearts with joy

REGENT SQUARE   87 87 87

Words: from Psalm 147
Timothy Dudley-Smith
Music: H T Smart (1813–79)

Fill your hearts with joy and glad-ness, sing and praise your
God and mine! Great the Lord in___ love and wis-dom,
might and ma-jes-ty di-vine! He who framed the
star-ry hea-vens knows and names them_ as they shine.

1 Fill your hearts with joy and gladness,
   sing and praise your God and mine!
   Great the Lord in love and wisdom,
   might and majesty divine!
   He who framed the starry heavens
   knows and names them as they shine.

2 Praise the Lord, His people, praise Him!
   wounded souls His comfort know;
   those who fear Him find His mercies,
   peace for pain and joy for woe;
   humble hearts are high exalted,
   human pride and power laid low.

3 Praise the Lord for times and seasons,
   cloud and sunshine, wind and rain;
   spring to melt the snows of winter
   till the waters flow again;
   grass upon the mountain pastures,
   golden valleys thick with grain.

4 Fill your hearts with joy and gladness,
   peace and plenty crown your days;
   love His laws, declare His judgements,
   walk in all His words and ways;
   He the Lord and we His children –
   praise the Lord, all people, praise!

148 For all the Saints

SINE NOMINE 10 10 10 4

(Words: W W How (1823–97))

Words: W W How (1823–97)
Music: R Vaughan Williams (1872–1958)

For all the Saints who from their la-bours rest,

who Thee by faith be - fore the world con - fessed,

Thy name, O Je - su, be for ev - er___ blest.

Al - le - lu - ia, al - le - lu - ia!

Music: © Oxford University Press
From the *English Hymnal*

1 For all the Saints who from their labours rest,
  who Thee by faith before the world confessed,
  Thy name, O Jesu, be for ever blest.
  Alleluia!

2 Thou wast their Rock, their fortress, and their might;
  Thou, Lord, their Captain in the well fought fight;
  Thou in the darkness drear their one true light.
  Alleluia!

3 O may Thy soldiers, faithful, true and bold,
  fight as the Saints who nobly fought of old,
  and win, with them, the victor's crown of gold!
  Alleluia!

4 O blest communion, fellowship divine!
  We feebly struggle, they in glory shine;
  yet all are one in Thee, for all are Thine.
  Alleluia!

5 And when the strife is fierce, the warfare long,
  steals on the ear the distant triumph song,
  and hearts are brave again, and arms are strong.
  Alleluia!

6 The golden evening brightens in the west;
  soon, soon to faithful warriors cometh rest;
  sweet is the calm of paradise the blest.
  Alleluia!

7 But lo! there breaks a yet more glorious day:
  the Saints triumphant rise in bright array;
  the King of glory passes on His way.
  Alleluia!

8 From earth's wide bounds, from ocean's farthest coast,
  through gates of pearl streams in the countless host,
  singing to Father, Son and Holy Ghost.
  Alleluia!

149   For God so loved the world

Words and music: Graham Kendrick
Music arranged Christopher Norton

WOMEN

1 For God so loved the world
that He gave His only Son;
and all who believe in Him
shall not die,
but have eternal life;
no, they shall not die,
but have eternal life.

ALL

2 And God showed His love for you,
when He gave His only Son;
and you, if you trust in Him,
shall not die,
but have eternal life;
no you shall not die,
but have eternal life.

150   For His name is exalted

Words and music: Dale Garratt
Music arranged David Peacock

For His name is ex-alt-ed,_____ His
glo-ry a-bove hea-ven and earth._____
Ho-ly is the Lord God al-migh-ty, who
was and who is and who is to come.

151 For I'm building a people of power

Words and music: Dave Richards
Music arranged Roger Mayor

For I'm build - ing a peo - ple of pow - er___ and I'm

mak - ing a peo - ple of praise, that will move through this land by My

Spi - rit,___ and will glo - ri - fy My pre - cious name. Build Your

Church, Lord, make us strong, Lord, join our hearts, Lord, through Your

152 For the beauty of the earth

ENGLAND's LANE 77 77 77

Words: Folliott Pierpoint (1835–1917)
altered Horrobin/Leavers
Music: from an English melody
adapted by Geoffrey Shaw (1879–1943)

For the beauty of the earth, for the beauty of the skies, for the love which from our birth over and around us lies; Father, unto You we raise this our sacrifice of praise.

1 For the beauty of the earth,
   for the beauty of the skies,
   for the love which from our birth
   over and around us lies;
   Father, unto You we raise
   this our sacrifice of praise.

2 For the beauty of each hour
   of the day and of the night,
   hill and vale, and tree and flower,
   sun and moon, and stars of light;
   Father, unto You we raise
   this our sacrifice of praise.

3 For the joy of love from God,
   that we share on earth below;
   for our friends and family,
   and the love that they can show;
   Father, unto You we raise
   this our sacrifice of praise.

4 For each perfect gift divine
   to our race so freely given,
   thank You Lord that they are mine,
   here on earth as gifts from heaven;
   Father, unto You we raise
   this our sacrifice of praise.

153   For the fruits of His creation

EAST ACKLAM   84 84 88 84

Words: F Pratt Green
Music: Francis Jackson

Words: © Stainer & Bell Ltd,
82 High Road, London N2 9PW

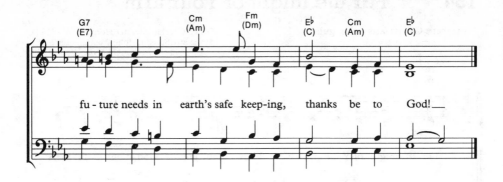

fu - ture needs in   earth's safe keep-ing,   thanks   be   to   God!___

1   For the fruits of His creation,
    thanks be to God!
    For His gifts to every nation,
    thanks be to God!
    For the ploughing, sowing, reaping,
    silent growth while we are sleeping;
    future needs in earth's safe keeping,
    thanks be to God!

2   In the just reward of labour,
    God's will is done;
    in the help we give our neighbour,
    God's will is done;
    in our worldwide task of caring
    for the hungry and despairing;
    in the harvests we are sharing,
    God's will is done.

3   For the harvests of the Spirit,
    thanks be to God!
    For the good we all inherit,
    thanks be to God!
    For the wonders that astound us,
    for the truths that still confound us;
    most of all, that love has found us,
    thanks be to God!

154 For the might of Your arm

MOUNTAIN CHRISTIANS Irregular

Words: Charles Silvester Horne (1865–1914)
Music: attributed to John Mannin (1802–65)
in the *Fellowship Hymn Book*, 1909

For the might of Your arm we bless You, our God, our_ fa-thers'
God; You have kept Your pil-grim peo-ple by the
strength of Your staff and rod; You have called us to the
jour-ney which faith-less feet ne'er trod;_____ *For the*

might of Your arm we__ bless You, our God, our__ fa - thers' God.

1 For the might of Your arm we bless You,
   our God, our fathers' God;
   You have kept Your pilgrim people
   by the strength of Your staff and rod;
   You have called us to the journey
   which faithless feet ne'er trod;
     For the might of Your arm we bless You,
     our God, our fathers' God.

2 For the love of Christ constraining,
   that bound their hearts as one;
   for the faith in truth and freedom
   in which their work was done;
   for the peace of God's evangel
   wherewith their feet were shod;
     For the might . . .

3 We are watchers of a beacon
   whose light must never die;
   we are guardians of an altar
   that shows You ever nigh;
   we are children of Your freemen
   who sleep beneath the sod;
     For the might . . .

4 May the shadow of Your presence
   around our camp be spread;
   baptize us with the courage
   You gave unto our dead;
   O keep us in the pathway
   their saintly feet have trod;
     For the might . . .

155 For this purpose

Words and music: Graham Kendrick
Music arranged David Peacock

1 For this pur-pose Christ was re-vealed, to des-troy all the works of the e-vil one. Christ in us has o-ver-come, so with

2 In the name of Je-sus we stand; by the power of His blood we now claim this ground: Sa-tan has no au-tho-ri-ty here, powers of

Words and music: © 1985 Make Way Music,
administered in Europe by Thankyou Music,
PO Box 75, Eastbourne, East Sussex BN23 6NW, UK

glad-ness we sing_____ and wel-come His king-dom in._____
dark-ness must flee,_____ for Christ has the vic-to-ry._____

MEN   WOMEN
_____ O - ver sin   He has con-quered: Hal-le -

                          MEN   WOMEN
- lu - jah! He has con-quered. O-ver death   vic - to - rious: Hal-le -

                     MEN   WOMEN
- lu - jah! vic - tor - ious. O - ver sick - ness He has tri-umphed: Hal-le -

ALL

- lu-jah! He has tri-umphed. *Je - sus reigns_____ o - ver*

all!_____

1 For this purpose Christ was revealed,
   to destroy all the works of the evil one.
   Christ in us has overcome,
   so with gladness we sing
   and welcome His kingdom in.
   MEN   *Over sin He has conquered:*
   WOMEN *Hallelujah! He has conquered.*
   MEN   *Over death victorious:*
   WOMEN *Hallelujah! victorious.*
   MEN   *Over sickness He has triumphed:*
   WOMEN *Hallelujah! He has triumphed.*
   ALL   *Jesus reigns over all!*

2 In the name of Jesus we stand;
   by the power of His blood
   we now claim this ground:
   Satan has no authority here,
   powers of darkness must flee,
   for Christ has the victory.
              Over sin . . .

156   For unto us a child is born

Words: from Isaiah 9
Music: Unknown
arranged Phil Burt

For un-to us a child is born,____ un-to us a Son is giv-en;____ and the gov-ern-ment shall be up-on His shoul-ders. And His name shall be called Won-der-ful, Coun-sel-lor, the Migh-ty God,____ the ev-er-last-ing Fa-ther, and the Prince of Peace is He.____

157 For unto us a child is born

Words and music: David J Hadden

158   # For Thou, O Lord

Words and music: Pete Sanchez Jnr

For Thou, O Lord, art high a-bove all the earth;_____ Thou art ex - alt - ed far a-bove all__ gods._____ For Thou, O -bove all gods._____ I ex -

For Thou, O Lord,
art high above all the earth;
Thou art exalted far above all gods.
For Thou, O Lord,
art high above all the earth;
Thou art exalted far above all gods.
I exalt Thee, I exalt Thee,
I exalt Thee, O Lord;
I exalt Thee, I exalt Thee,
I exalt Thee, O Lord.

159 Forth in Thy name, O Lord, I go

ANGEL'S SONG   LM

Words: Charles Wesley (1707–88)
Music: Orlando Gibbons (1583–1625)

Forth in Thy name, O Lord, I go, my dai-ly la-bour to pur-sue, Thee, on-ly Thee, re-solved to know in all I think, or speak, or do.

1 Forth in Thy name, O Lord, I go,
my daily labour to pursue,
Thee, only Thee, resolved to know
in all I think, or speak, or do.

2 The task Thy wisdom hath assigned
O let me cheerfully fulfil;
in all my works Thy presence find,
and prove Thy acceptable will.

3 Thee may I set at my right hand,
whose eyes my inmost substance see;
and labour on at Thy command,
and offer all my works to Thee.

4 Give me to bear Thy easy yoke,
and every moment watch and pray,
and still to things eternal look,
and hasten to Thy glorious day.

5 For Thee delightfully employ
whate'er Thy bounteous grace hath given,
and run my course with even joy,
and closely walk with Thee to heaven.

160 Forty days and forty nights

HEINLEIN 77 77

Words: G H Smyttan (1822–70) altd.
Music: M Herbst (1654–81)

1 Forty days and forty nights
Thou wast fasting in the wild;
forty days and forty nights
tempted and yet undefiled.

2 Sunbeams scorching all the day,
chilly dew-drops nightly shed,
prowling beasts about Thy way,
stones Thy pillow, earth Thy bed.

3 Let us Thy endurance share
and from earthly greed abstain,
with Thee watching unto prayer,
with Thee strong to suffer pain.

4 Then if evil on us press,
flesh or spirit to assail,
victor in the wilderness,
may we never faint or fail!

5 So shall peace divine be ours;
holier gladness ours shall be;
come to us angelic powers,
such as ministered to Thee.

161   Freely, for the love He bears us

Words: Timothy Dudley-Smith
Music: Phil Burt

Free-ly, for the love He bears us, God has made His pur-pose plain:

Christ has died and Christ is ris-en, Christ will come a - gain.

1 Freely, for the love He bears us,
   God has made His purpose plain:
   Christ has died and Christ is risen,
   Christ will come again.

2 Christ has died, the world's Redeemer,
   Lamb of God for sinners slain:
   Christ has died . . .

3 Christ is risen, high-ascended,
   Lord of all to rule and reign:
   Christ has died . . .

4 Christ is coming, King of Glory,
   firmly then the faith maintain:
   Christ has died . . .

162 From heaven You came

THE SERVANT KING

Words and music: Graham Kendrick
Music arranged David Peacock

Worshipfully

Capo 3(Am)

1 From heaven You came, help-less babe, en-tered our world, Your
2 There in the gar-den of tears my hea-vy load He
3 Come see His hands and His feet, the scars that speak of
4 So let us learn how to serve and in our lives en-

glo - ry veiled, not to be served but to serve,
chose to bear; His heart with sor - row was torn,
sac - ri - fice, hands that flung stars in - to space,
- throne Him, each o - ther's needs to pre - fer,

and give Your life that we might live.
'Yet not my will but yours,' He said.
to cru - el nails sur - rend - ered.
for it is Christ we're serv - ing.

This is our

Part II *This is our God,* *the Ser-vant King,* *He calls us now to*

God,_____ the Ser-vant King,_____ He calls us now to fol-low

fol-low Him,__ *to bring our lives* *an off-er-ing*

Him,_____ to bring our lives as a dai-ly of-fer - ing_____ of wor-ship

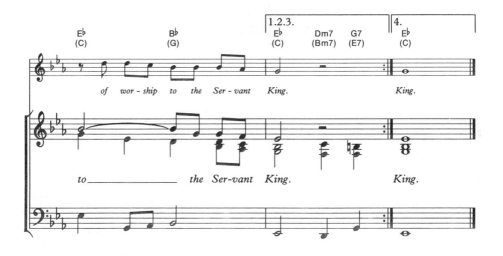

of wor-ship to the Ser - vant King. *King.*

to_____ the Ser-vant King. *King.*

163   From the rising of the sun

Words and music: Paul Deming

praise Him O ye ser-vants of the Lord, praise the

name of the Lord; bless-ed be the

name of the Lord from this time forth,

and for ev - er - more._____

164   From the sun's rising

Words and music: Graham Kendrick
Music arranged Christopher Norton

1 From the sun's ris-ing un - to the sun's set-ting, Je - sus our Lord shall be great in the earth; and all earth's king-doms shall be His do - mi-nion – all of cre - a - tion shall sing of His worth. Let ev-ery heart, ev-ery voice,_ ev-ery tongue join with spi - rits a - blaze; one in His love, we will cir - cle the world with the

2 To every tongue, tribe and nation He sends us,
   to make disciples, to teach and baptize;
   for all authority to Him is given;
   now as His witnesses we shall arise.
        Let every heart . . .

3 Come let us join with the Church from all nations,
   cross every border, throw wide every door;
   workers with Him as He gathers His harvest,
   till earth's far corners our Saviour adore.
        Let every heart . . .

        *Let all His people rejoice,
        and let all the earth hear His voice!*

165

Give me a heart

Words and music: G E Hutchinson

Give me a heart that will love the un-love-ly,
o-pen my eyes to the nee-dy and lost,
help me, O Lord, to show Your love in ac-tion,
give, with-out count-ing the cost,

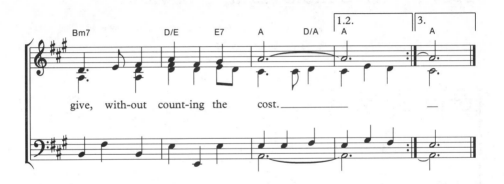

give, with-out count-ing the cost._____ __

1 Give me a heart that will love the unlovely,
   open my eyes to the needy and lost,
   help me, O Lord, to show Your love in action,
   give, without counting the cost,
   give, without counting the cost.

2 Help me remember I'm empty without You,
   help me to find my strength only in You.
   I can give nothing unless You first fill me,
   Your love alone must shine through,
   Your love alone must shine through.

3 Make me be willing to go where You send me,
   make me be ready to answer Your call.
   Give me a heart that rejoices to serve You,
   sharing the best love of all,
   sharing the best love of all.

166 Give me a sight, O Saviour

Words and music: Katherine Agnes May Kelly (1869–1942)

help me to take it in;_____ what it meant to Thee, the

Ho - ly One, to bear___ a - way my sin._____

1 Give me a sight, O Saviour,
   of Thy wondrous love to me,
   of the love that brought Thee down to earth,
   to die on Calvary.
   O make me understand it,
   help me to take it in;
   what it meant to Thee,
   the Holy One,
   to bear away my sin.

2 Was it the nails, O Saviour,
   that bound Thee to the tree?
   Nay, 'twas Thine everlasting love,
   Thy love for me, for me.
   O make me understand . . .

3 O wonder of all wonders,
   that through Thy death for me
   my open sins, my secret sins,
   can all forgiven be!
   O make me understand . . .

4 Then melt my heart, O Saviour,
   bend me, yes, break me down,
   until I own Thee – Conqueror,
   and Lord, and Sovereign crown.
   O make me understand . . .

167   Give me oil in my lamp

Words and music: Anon
Music arranged Betty Pulkingham

1 Give me oil in my lamp, keep me burn-ing,_____ give me
2 Make me a fish - er of men, keep me seek-ing,_____ make me a
3 Give me joy in my heart, keep me sing-ing,_____ give me
4 Give me love in my heart, keep me serv-ing,_____ give me

oil in my lamp, I pray; give me
fish - er of men, I pray; make me a
joy in my heart, I pray; give me
love in my heart, I pray; give me

oil in my lamp, keep me burn - ing,_____ keep me
fish - er of men, keep me seek - ing,_____ keep me
joy in my heart, keep me sing - ing,_____ keep me
love in my heart, keep me serv - ing,_____ keep me

burn - ing till the break of day.
seek - ing till the break of day.
sing - ing till the break of day.
serv - ing till the break of day.

Words and music: Copyright control
Music arrangement © 1974, 1975 Celebration,
administered in Europe by Thankyou Music,
PO Box 75, Eastbourne, East Sussex BN23 6NW, UK

Sing ho-san-na, sing ho-san-na,

sing ho-san-na to the King of kings! King. (2) Make

1 Give me oil in my lamp, keep me burning,
  give me oil in my lamp, I pray;
  give me oil in my lamp, keep me burning,
  keep me burning till the break of day.
    Sing hosanna, sing hosanna,
    sing hosanna to the King of kings!
    Sing hosanna, sing hosanna,
    sing hosanna to the King.

2 Make me a fisher of men, keep me seeking,
  make me a fisher of men, I pray;
  make me a fisher of men, keep me seeking,
  keep me seeking till the break of day.
    Sing hosanna . . .

3 Give me joy in my heart, keep me singing,
  give me joy in my heart, I pray;
  give me joy in my heart, keep me singing,
  keep me singing till the break of day.
    Sing hosanna . . .

4 Give me love in my heart, keep me serving,
  give me love in my heart, I pray;
  give me love in my heart, keep me serving,
  keep me serving till the break of day.
    Sing hosanna . . .

168 Give me the faith

GIESSEN   88 88 88

Words: Charles Wesley (1707–88)
Music: from Gauntlett's *Comprehensive Tune Book*, 1851

- power, let it___ my ran - somed soul___ de - vour.

1 Give me the faith which can remove
and sink the mountain to a plain;
give me the childlike, praying love,
which longs to build Thy house again;
Thy love let it my heart o'erpower,
let it my ransomed soul devour.

2 I would the precious time redeem,
and longer live for this alone –
to spend and to be spent for them
who have not yet my Saviour known;
fully on these my mission prove,
and only breathe to breathe Thy love.

3 My talents, gifts, and graces, Lord,
into Thy blessèd hands receive;
and let me live to preach Thy word,
and let me to Thy glory live;
my every sacred moment spend
in publishing the sinners' friend.

4 Enlarge, inflame, and fill my heart
with boundless charity divine;
so shall I all my strength exert,
and love them with a zeal like Thine;
and lead them to Thine open side,
the sheep for whom their Shepherd died.

169   # Give thanks to the Lord

Words and music: Mark Hayes

1 Give thanks to the Lord for He is good,
(2) un - der - stand - ing made the heavens, His
(3) child - ren through the wil - der - ness, His
(4) - mem-bered us in our low es - tate,

love en - dures for ev - er. Give thanks to the God
And made the great and shin -
And struck down ma - ny migh -
And freed us from our en -

- of gods,
- ing lights,
- ty kings, His love en - dures for ev - er. The
- e - mies, And
To

O give thanks__ to the Lord of lords,
might-y sun____ to__ rule the day,_ His love en-dures for__
gave to them an in - he - ri - tance,
ev - ery crea - ture_ He gives food,

ev - er.
To__ Him a - lone_ who does__ great works,
And the moon and the stars to rule__ at__ night. His
A pro-mised land_ for Is - ra - el,__ His
Give thanks to the God__ of__ heaven,

last time **to Coda**

love en-dures for ev - er.
2 By His
- er.
- er.

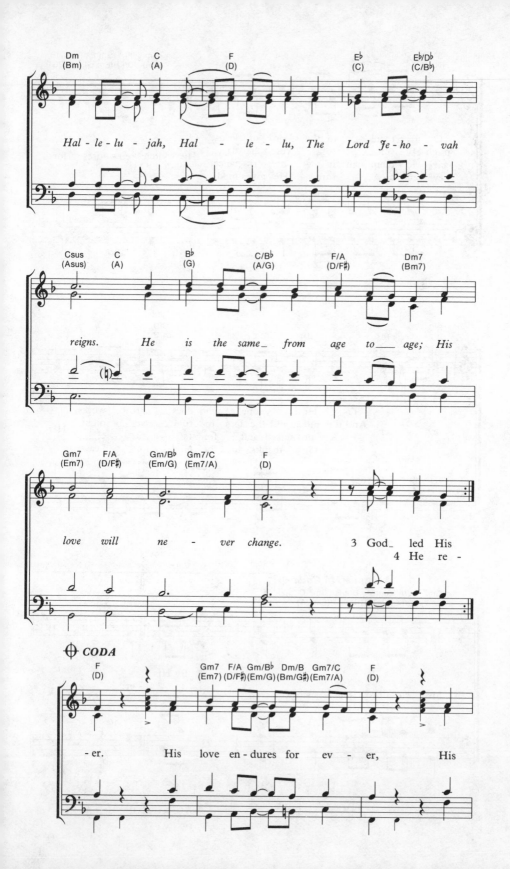

1 Give thanks to the Lord for He is good,
His love endures for ever.
Give thanks to the God of gods,
His love endures for ever.
O give thanks to the Lord of lords,
His love endures for ever.
To Him alone who does great works,
His love endures for ever.

2 By His understanding made the heavens,
His love endures for ever.
Who made the great and shining lights,
His love endures for ever.
The mighty sun to rule the day,
His love endures for ever.
And the moon and the stars to rule at night,
His love endures for ever.
   Hallelujah, Hallelu,
   The Lord Jehovah reigns.
   He is the same from age to age;
   His love will never change.

3 God led His children through the
         wilderness,
His love endures for ever.
And struck down many mighty kings,
His love endures for ever.
And gave to them an inheritance,
His love endures for ever.
A promised land for Israel,
His love endures for ever.
   Hallelujah . . .

4 He remembered us in our low estate,
His love endures for ever.
And freed us from our enemies,
His love endures for ever.
To every creature He gives food,
His love endures for ever.
Give thanks to the God of heaven,
His love endures for ever,
His love endures for ever,
His love endures for ever.

170   Give thanks with a grateful heart

Words and music: Henry Smith
Music arranged David Peacock

171   Give to our God immortal praise

RIMINGTON   LM

Words: Isaac Watts (1674–1748) altd.
Music: F Duckworth (1862–1941)

1   Give to our God immortal praise;
  mercy and truth are all His ways:
  wonders of grace to God belong,
  repeat His mercies in your song.

2   Give to the Lord of lords renown;
  the King of kings with glory crown:
  His mercies ever shall endure,
  when lords and kings are known no more.

3   He built the earth, He spread the sky,
  and fixed the starry lights on high:
  wonders of grace to God belong,
  repeat His mercies in your song.

4   He fills the sun with morning light,
  He bids the moon direct the night:
  His mercies ever shall endure,
  when suns and moons shall shine no more.

5   He sent His Son with power to save
  from guilt and darkness and the grave:
  wonders of grace to God belong,
  repeat His mercies in your song.

172 Glorious Father

Words and music: Danny Reed

Glo - ri-ous Fa-ther we ex - alt__ You; we wor - ship, hon-our and a - dore__ You; we de - light to be__ in Your pres - ence O Lord. We mag - ni - fy__ Your ho - ly name, and we sing come Lord Je - sus, glo - ri - fy Your name, and we sing come Lord Je - sus, glo - ri - fy Your name.

Words and music: © 1987 Thankyou Music,
PO Box 75, Eastbourne, East Sussex BN23 6NW, UK

173 Glorious things of thee are spoken

AUSTRIA 87 87 D

Words: John Newton (1725–1807)
Music: J F Haydn (1732–1809)

Glo-rious things of thee are spo-ken, Zi - on, ci - ty of our God;

He, whose word can - not be bro-ken, formed thee for His own a - bode:

on the Rock of A - ges found-ed, what can__ shake thy sure re-pose?

With sal-va-tion's walls sur - round-ed, thou may'st smile at__ all thy foes.

1 Glorious things of thee are spoken,
   Zion, city of our God;
   He, whose word cannot be broken,
   formed thee for His own abode:
   on the Rock of ages founded,
   what can shake thy sure repose?
   With salvation's walls surrounded,
   thou may'st smile at all thy foes.

2 See, the streams of living waters,
   springing from eternal love,
   well supply thy sons and daughters
   and all fear of want remove:
   who can faint, while such a river
   ever flows their thirst to assuage?
   Grace which, like the Lord, the giver,
   never fails from age to age.

3 Saviour, if of Zion's city
   I, through grace, a member am,
   let the world deride or pity,
   I will glory in Thy name:
   fading is the worldling's pleasure,
   all his boasted pomp and show;
   solid joys and lasting treasure
   none but Zion's children know.

174 Glory, glory in the highest

Words and music: Danny Daniels

glo - ry,___ WOMEN glo - ry,___ MEN glo - ry,___ WOMEN glo - ry,_____

MEN glo - ry,___ ALL glo - ry to the___ Lamb!___ MEN I give

2nd time **to Coda** ⊕   *D.%̸ al Coda*

ALL I give glo - ry to___ the Lamb!

⊕ *CODA*

I give glo - ry to___ the Lamb!

175   Glory be to God in heaven

REGENT SQUARE   87 87 87

Words: John Richards
Music: H Smart (1813–79)

Capo 2(G)

1 Glo-ry be to God in hea-ven, and to all on
2 Christ in-car-nate, sent by Fa-ther to re-deem, re-

earth, His peace; Lord and Fa-ther,_ King in glo-ry,
-new, re-store; ris-en Lamb, in_ glo-ry seat-ed,

gifts of praise in_ us re-lease, so our wor-ship
hear our prayers Lord, we im-plore. Now to Fa-ther,

and thanks-giv-ing from our hearts will_ ne-ver cease.
Son, and Spi-rit be all glo-ry_ ev-er-more.

176 # Glory to You, my God

TALLIS' CANON   LM

Words: T Ken (1637–1710)
in this version Jubilate Hymns
Music: Thomas Tallis (1505–1585)

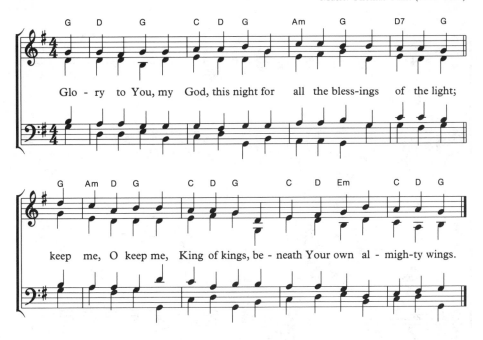

Glo - ry to You, my God, this night for all the bless-ings of the light;

keep me, O keep me, King of kings, be - neath Your own al - migh-ty wings.

1 Glory to You, my God, this night
  for all the blessings of the light;
  keep me, O keep me, King of kings,
  beneath Your own almighty wings.

2 Forgive me, Lord, through Your dear Son,
  the wrong that I this day have done,
  that peace with God and man may be,
  before I sleep, restored to me.

3 Teach me to live, that I may dread
  the grave as little as my bed;
  teach me to die, that so I may
  rise glorious at the awesome day.

4 O may my soul on you repose
  and restful sleep my eyelids close;
  sleep that shall me more vigorous make
  to serve my God when I awake.

5 If in the night I sleepless lie,
  my mind with peaceful thoughts supply;
  let no dark dreams disturb my rest,
  no powers of evil me molest.

6 Praise God from whom all blessings flow
  in heaven above and earth below;
  one God, three persons, we adore –
  to Him be praise for evermore!

177 Glory to God in the highest

Words and music: Greg Leavers
Music arranged Phil Burt

Glory to God in the highest,
peace upon earth,
Jesus Christ has come to earth;
that's why we sing,
Jesus the King,
Jesus has come for you.

1 The shepherds who were sitting there
   were suddenly filled with fear;
   the dark night was filled with light,
   angels singing everywhere.
       Glory to God . . .

2 The next time we hear a song
   of worship from a heavenly throng,
   will be when Jesus comes again,
   then with triumph we'll all sing:
       Glory to God . . .

178 Go forth and tell

YANWORTH 10 10 10 10

Words: J E Seddon (1915–83)
Music: John Barnard

Go forth and tell! O Church of God, a-wake! God's sav-ing news to all the na-tions take:_____ pro-claim Christ Je-sus, Sav-iour, Lord and king,_____ that all the world His wor-thy praise may sing._____

1 Go forth and tell! O Church of God, awake!
God's saving news to all the nations take:
proclaim Christ Jesus, Saviour, Lord and King,
that all the world His worthy praise may sing.

2 Go forth and tell! God's love embraces all;
He will in grace respond to all who call:
how shall they call if they have never heard
the gracious invitation of His word?

3 Go forth and tell! men still in darkness lie;
in wealth or want, in sin they live and die:
give us, O Lord, concern of heart and mind,
a love like Yours which cares for all mankind.

4 Go forth and tell! the doors are open wide:
share God's good gifts – let no one be denied;
live out your life as Christ your Lord shall choose,
Your ransomed powers for His sole glory use.

5 Go forth and tell! O church of God, arise!
Go in the strength which Christ your Lord supplies;
go till all nations His great name adore
and serve Him, Lord and King for evermore.

179 Go, tell it on the mountain

Words and music: Geoffrey Marshall-Taylor
Music arranged: Douglas Coombes

Go, tell it on the moun - tain, o-ver the hills and ev-ery-where;

go, tell it on the moun - tain that Je - sus is His name.

He pos-sessed no rich-es, no home to lay His head; He

saw the needs of oth-ers and cared for them in - stead.___

Go, tell it on the mountain,
over the hills and everywhere;
go, tell it on the mountain
that Jesus is His name.

1 He possessed no riches, no home to lay His head;
  He saw the needs of others and cared for them instead.
    Go tell it on the mountain . . .

2 He reached out and touched them, the blind, the deaf, the lame;
  He spoke and listened gladly to anyone who came.
    Go tell it on the mountain . . .

3 Some turned away in anger, with hatred in the eye;
  they tried Him and condemned Him, then led Him out to die.
    Go tell it on the mountain . . .

4 'Father, now forgive them' – those were the words He said;
  in three more days He was alive and risen from the dead.
    Go tell it on the mountain . . .

5 He still comes to people, His life moves through the lands;
  He uses us for speaking, He touches with our hands.
    Go tell it on the mountain . . .

180 God came among us

Words and music: Marilyn Baker
Music arranged Phil Burt

God came a - mong us, He be - came a man,

be - came a ba - by, though through Him the world be - gan.

He came to earth to bring us peace, but

where is that peace to - day?___ It can be found

by those who will let Him dir-ect their way.

- lieve.

1 God came among us, He became a man,
   became a baby, though through Him the world began.
   He came to earth to bring us peace,
   but where is that peace today?
   It can be found
   by those who will let Him direct their way.

2 He came to serve, to show us how much He cared;
   our joys and sorrows He so willingly shared.
   He came to earth to bring us joy,
   but where is that joy today?
   It can be found
   by those who let Him wash their guilt away.

3 Death tried to hold Him, but it could not succeed;
   He rose again, and now we can be freed.
   He longs to give eternal life
   to all who will simply receive,
   yes to all who
   will open their hearts and just believe.

181   God forgave my sin

Words and music: Carol Owens

1 God for - gave   my sin   in Je - sus'
2 All   power   is given   in Je - sus'

name;   I've been born   a - gain   in
name   in   earth   and heaven   in

Je - sus' name,   and in Je - sus'
Je - sus' name;   and in Je - sus'

name   I come   to you   to
name   I come   to you   to

182 God has spoken to His people

Words: Willard Jabusch
Music: Israeli folk melody
arranged Norman Warren

God has spo-ken to His peo-ple, al-le-lu - ia,

and His words are words of wis-dom, al-le-lu - ia!

O - pen your ears, O Christ-ian peo-ple, o - pen your ears and hear good news;

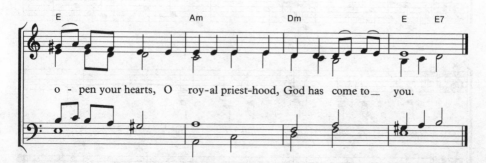

o - pen your hearts, O roy-al priest-hood, God has come to_ you.

God has spoken to His people, alleluia,
and His words are words of wisdom, alleluia!

1   Open your ears, O Christian people,
    open your ears and hear good news;
    open your hearts, O royal priesthood,
    God has come to you.
        God has spoken . . .

2   They who have ears to hear His message,
    they who have ears, then let them hear;
    they who would learn the way of wisdom,
    let them hear God's word!
        God has spoken . . .

3   Israel comes to greet the Saviour,
    Judah is glad to see His day;
    from east and west the peoples travel,
    He will show the way.
        God has spoken . . .

183 God holds the key

Words: Joseph Parker (1830–1902)
Music: George C Stebbins (1846–1945)

1 God holds the key of all unknown,
  and I am glad:
  if other hands should hold the key,
  or if He trusted it to me,
  I might be sad, I might be sad.

2 What if tomorrow's cares were here
  without its rest?
  I'd rather He unlocked the day,
  and, as the hours swing open, say,
  'My will is best, My will is best.'

3 The very dimness of my sight
  makes me secure;
  for, groping in my misty way,
  I feel His hand; I hear Him say,
  'My help is sure, My help is sure.'

4 I cannot read His future plans;
  but this I know:
  I have the smiling of His face,
  and all the refuge of His grace,
  while here below, while here below.

5 Enough: this covers all my wants;
  and so I rest!
  for what I cannot, He can see,
  and in His care I saved shall be,
  for ever blest, for ever blest.

184 God is building a house

Words and music: Anon
Music arranged Phil Burt

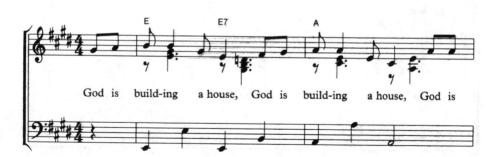

God is build-ing a house, God is build-ing a house, God is

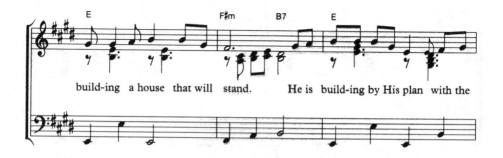

build-ing a house that will stand. He is build-ing by His plan with the

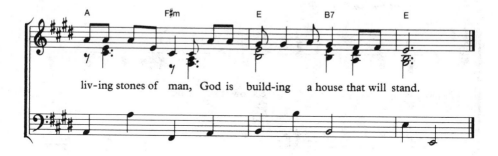

liv-ing stones of man, God is build-ing a house that will stand.

1 God is building a house,
   God is building a house,
   God is building a house that will stand.
   He is building by His plan
   with the living stones of man,
   God is building a house that will stand.

2 God is building a house,
   God is building a house,
   God is building a house that will stand.
   With apostles, prophets, pastors,
   with evangelists and teachers,
   God is building a house that will stand.

3 Christ is head of this house,
   Christ is head of this house,
   Christ is head of this house that will stand.
   He abideth in its praise,
   will perfect it in its ways,
   Christ is head of this house that will stand.

4 We are part of this house,
   we are part of this house,
   we are part of this house that will stand.
   We are called from every nation
   to enjoy His full salvation,
   we are part of this house that will stand.

185 God is good

Words and music: Graham Kendrick
Music arranged David Peacock

God is good – we sing and shout it, __ God is good –
we ce-le-brate; God is good – no more we doubt it, __
God is good – we know it's true!
And when I think of His love for me, my heart fills with praise and I

feel like danc - ing; for in His heart there is room for me, and I

run with arms o-pened wide._____

⊕ CODA

we know it's true! *Hey!*

God is good – we sing and shout it,
God is good – we celebrate;
God is good – no more we doubt it,
God is good – we know it's true!

And when I think of His love for me,
my heart fills with praise
and I feel like dancing;
for in His heart there is room for me,
and I run with arms opened wide.

God is good – we sing and shout it,
God is good – we celebrate;
God is good – no more we doubt it,
God is good – we know it's true! *Hey!*

186 God is in His temple

GRÖNINGEN   668 668 33 66

Words: W T Matson (1833–99)
Music: J Neander (1650–80)

God is in His tem - ple, the Al - migh - ty
Fa - ther, round His foot-stool let us ga - ther:
Him with a - dor - a - tion serve, the Lord most
ho - ly, who has mer - cy on the low - ly:

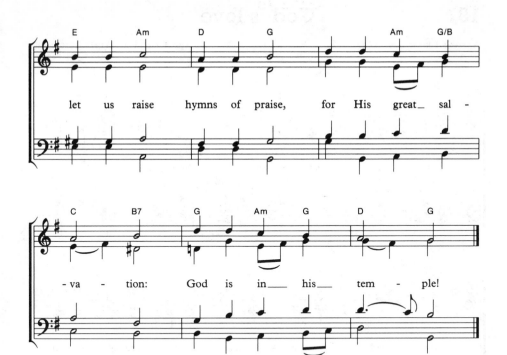

let us raise hymns of praise, for His great salvation: God is in his temple!

1 God is in His temple,
  the Almighty Father,
  round His footstool let us gather:
  Him with adoration
  serve, the Lord most holy,
  who has mercy on the lowly:
    let us raise
    hymns of praise,
  for His great salvation:
    God is in His temple!

2 Christ comes to His temple:
  we, His word receiving,
  are made happy in believing.
  Lo! from sin delivered,
  He has turned our sadness,
  our deep gloom, to light and gladness!
    let us raise
    hymns of praise,
  for our bonds are severed:
    Christ comes to His temple!

3 Come and claim Your temple,
  gracious Holy Spirit!
  In our hearts Your home inherit:
  make in us Your dwelling,
  Your high work fulfilling,
  into ours Your will instilling,
    till we raise
    hymns of praise
  beyond mortal telling,
    in the eternal temple.

187   God is love

ABBOT'S LEIGH   87 87 D

Words: Timothy Rees (1874–1939) altd.
Music: Cyril Taylor

God_ is love: let heaven_ a - dore Him;_ God_ is

love:_ let earth re - joice;_ let cre - a - tion

sing_ be - fore Him, and_ ex - alt_ Him with_ one voice.

He_ who laid_ the earth's_ foun - da - tion,_ He_ who

spread   the   heavens a - bove,   He___ who breathes through

all___ cre - a - tion,_   He__   is   love,_   e - ter - nal love.

1 God is love: let heaven adore Him;
   God is love: let earth rejoice;
   let creation sing before Him,
   and exalt Him with one voice.
   He who laid the earth's foundation,
   He who spread the heavens above,
   He who breathes through all creation,
   He is love, eternal love.

2 God is love: and He enfoldeth
   all the world in one embrace;
   with unfailing grasp He holdeth
   every child of every race.
   And when human hearts are breaking
   under sorrow's iron rod,
   all the sorrow, all the aching,
   wrings with pain the heart of God.

3 God is love: and though with blindness
   sin afflicts the souls of men,
   God's eternal loving-kindness
   holds and guides them even then.
   Sin and death and hell shall never
   o'er us final triumph gain;
   God is love, so love for ever
   o'er the universe must reign.

188 God is our strength and refuge

DAMBUSTERS MARCH 77 75 77 11

Words: from Psalm 46
Richard Bewes
Music: E Coates (1886–1958)
arranged John Barnard

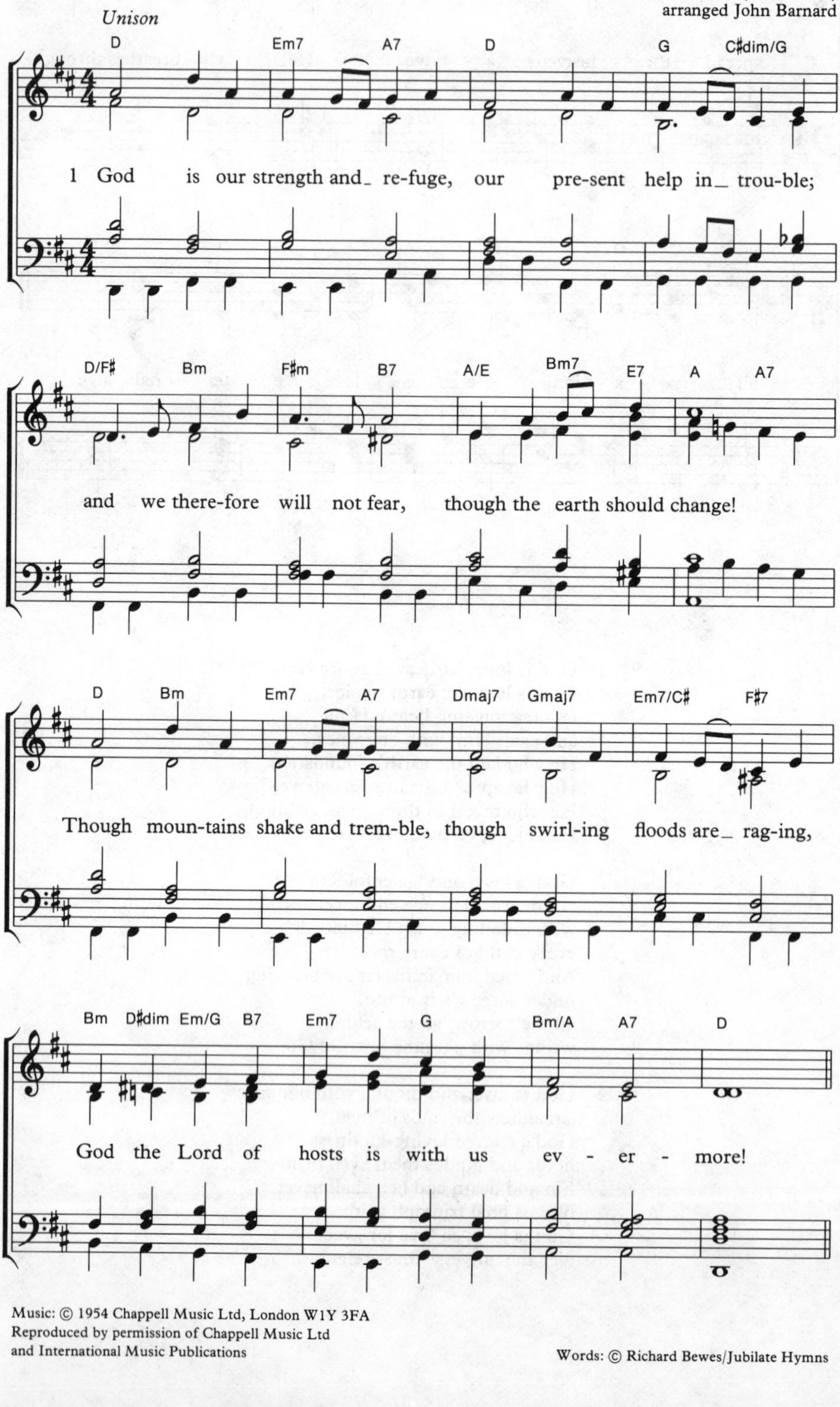
Unison
D Em7 A7 D G C♯dim/G
1 God is our strength and_ re-fuge, our pre-sent help in_ trou-ble;
D/F♯ Bm F♯m B7 A/E Bm7 E7 A A7
and we there-fore will not fear, though the earth should change!
D Bm Em7 A7 Dmaj7 Gmaj7 Em7/C♯ F♯7
Though moun-tains shake and trem-ble, though swirl-ing floods are_ rag-ing,
Bm D♯dim Em/G B7 Em7 G Bm/A A7 D
God the Lord of hosts is with us ev - er - more!

Harmony

D   Em7   A7   D   G   C#dim/G

2 There is a flow-ing_ ri-ver, with-in God's ho-ly_ ci-ty;
3 Come, see the works of our Mak-er, learn of His deeds all-power-ful;

D/F#   Bm   F#m   B7   A/E   Bm7   E7   A   A7

God is in the midst of her— she shall not_ be moved!_____
wars will cease a-cross the world when He shat-ters the spear!_____

D   Bm   Em7   A7   Dmaj7 Gmaj7   Em7/C#   F#

God's help is swift-ly_ giv-en, thrones van-ish at His pres-ence—
Be still and know your Cre-a-tor, up-lift Him in the_ na-tions—

Bm D#dim/A Em/G   B7   Em7   G   Bm/A   A7   D

God the Lord of hosts is with us ev-er-more!
God the Lord of hosts is with us ev-er-more!

189 God is working His purpose out

BENSON   Irregular

Words: A C Ainger (1841–1919)
in this version Jubilate Hymns
Music: Millicent D Kingham (1866–1927)

God is____ work-ing His pur-pose out, as____ year__ suc-ceeds to__ year: God is____ work-ing His pur-pose__ out, and the time is____ draw-ing__ near: near - er and near - er draws the____ time, the____

time that shall sure - ly be, when the earth shall be filled with the

glo - ry of God, as the wa - ters__ co - ver the sea.

1 God is working His purpose out,
as year succeeds to year:
God is working His purpose out,
and the time is drawing near:
nearer and nearer draws the time,
the time that shall surely be,
when the earth shall be filled
with the glory of God,
as the waters cover the sea.

2 From utmost east to utmost west
wherever man has trod,
by the mouth of many messengers
rings out the voice of God:
listen to me you continents,
you islands look to me,
that the earth may be filled
with the glory of God,
as the waters cover the sea.

3 We shall march in the strength of God,
with the banner of Christ unfurled,
that the light of the glorious gospel of truth
may shine throughout the world;
we shall fight with sorrow and sin
to set their captives free,
that the earth may be filled
with the glory of God,
as the waters cover the sea.

4 All we can do is nothing worth
unless God blesses the deed;
vainly we hope for the harvest-tide
till God gives life to the seed:
nearer and nearer draws the time,
the time that shall surely be,
when the earth shall be filled
with the glory of God,
as the waters cover the sea.

190 God of all ages

Words: Peter Coutts
Music: Peter Graham

The guitar chords are not compatible with the piano accompaniment

1 God of all ages and Lord for all time,
   Creator of all things in perfect design:
   for fields ripe for harvest, for rich golden grain,
   for beauty in nature, we thank You again.

2 God of all nations and Lord of all lands,
   who placed the world's wealth in the palm of our hands,
   we pray for Your guidance to guard against greed.
   though great the resources, still great is the need.

3 God of compassion and Lord of all life,
   we pray for Your people in conflict and strife.
   The earth You created a vast treasure store,
   yet hunger still thrives while men fight to gain more.

4 God of all wisdom, take us by the hand
   and insight bestow when we ruin Your land.
   For rivers polluted, for forests laid bare,
   we pray Your forgiveness for failing to care.

5 God of all greatness and giver of light,
   with each sunlit morning we worship Your might,
   our half-hearted service Your only reward:
   for love beyond measure, we thank You O Lord.

191 God of glory

Words and music: Dave Fellingham
Music arranged David Peacock

Lyrics:
God of glo-ry, we ex-alt Your name, You who reign in ma-jes-ty; we lift our hearts to You and we will wor-ship, praise, and mag-ni-fy Your ho-ly name. In power res-

192(i) God of grace and God of glory

WESTMINSTER ABBEY   87 87 87

Words: H E Fosdick (1878–1969)
Music: from *The Psalmist*, 1842
adapted from Henry Purcell (1659–95)

God of grace and God of glory, on Thy people pour Thy power; crown Thine an-cient Church's sto-ry; bring her bud to glor-ious flower. Grant us wis-dom, grant us cour-age, for the fac-ing of this hour.

1 God of grace and God of glory,
  on Thy people pour Thy power;
  crown Thine ancient Church's story;
  bring her bud to glorious flower.
  Grant us wisdom,
  grant us courage,
  for the facing of this hour.

2 Lo! the hosts of evil round us
  scorn Thy Christ, assail His ways!
  Fears and doubts too long have bound us;
  free our hearts to work and praise.
  Grant us wisdom,
  grant us courage,
  for the living of these days.

3 Heal Thy children's warring madness;
  bend our pride to Thy control;
  shame our wanton, selfish gladness,
  rich in things and poor in soul.
  Grant us wisdom,
  grant us courage,
  lest we miss Thy kingdom's goal.

4 Set our feet on lofty places;
  gird our lives that they may be
  armoured with all Christlike graces
  in the fight to set men free.
  Grant us wisdom,
  grant us courage,
  that we fail not man nor Thee.

5 Save us from weak resignation
  to the evils we deplore;
  let the search for Thy salvation
  be our glory evermore.
  Grant us wisdom,
  grant us courage,
  serving Thee whom we adore.

192(ii) God of grace and God of glory

RHUDDLAN   87 87 87

Words: H E Fosdick (1878–1969)
Music: Welsh traditional melody

God of grace and God of glory, on Thy peo - ple
pour Thy power;__ crown Thine an - cient Chur - ch's sto - ry;
bring her bud to glor - ious flower. Grant us wis - dom,__
grant us cour - age,__ for the fac - ing of this hour.

1   God of grace and God of glory,
     on Thy people pour Thy power;
     crown Thine ancient Church's story;
     bring her bud to glorious flower.
     Grant us wisdom,
     grant us courage,
     for the facing of this hour.

2   Lo! the hosts of evil round us
     scorn Thy Christ, assail His ways!
     Fears and doubts too long have bound us;
     free our hearts to work and praise.
     Grant us wisdom,
     grant us courage,
     for the living of these days.

3   Heal Thy children's warring madness;
     bend our pride to Thy control;
     shame our wanton, selfish gladness,
     rich in things and poor in soul.
     Grant us wisdom,
     grant us courage,
     lest we miss Thy kingdom's goal.

4   Set our feet on lofty places;
     gird our lives that they may be
     armoured with all Christlike graces
     in the fight to set men free.
     Grant us wisdom,
     grant us courage,
     that we fail not man nor Thee.

5   Save us from weak resignation
     to the evils we deplore;
     let the search for Thy salvation
     be our glory evermore.
     Grant us wisdom,
     grant us courage,
     serving Thee whom we adore.

193   God moves in a mysterious way

LONDON NEW   CM

Words: William Cowper (1731–1800)
Music: from *Playford's Psalms*, 1671
adapted from *Scottish Psalter*, 1635

God moves in a mys - ter - ious__ way, His
won - ders to__ per - form; He plants His__ foot - steps
in the__ sea, and rides up - on the storm.

1   God moves in a mysterious way,
His wonders to perform;
He plants His footsteps in the sea,
and rides upon the storm.

2   Deep in unfathomable mines
of never-failing skill,
He treasures up His bright designs,
and works His sovereign will.

3   Ye fearful saints, fresh courage take;
the clouds ye so much dread
are big with mercy, and shall break
in blessings on your head.

4   Judge not the Lord by feeble sense,
but trust Him for His grace;
behind a frowning providence
He hides a smiling face.

5   His purposes will ripen fast,
unfolding every hour;
the bud may have a bitter taste,
but sweet will be the flower.

6   Blind unbelief is sure to err,
and scan His work in vain;
God is His own interpreter,
and He will make it plain.

194   God save our gracious Queen

NATIONAL ANTHEM   664 6664

Words: Unknown
Music: *Thesaurus Musicus*, 1743

1   God save our gracious Queen,
long live our noble Queen,
God save the Queen!
Send her victorious,
happy and glorious,
long to reign over us;
God save the Queen!

2   Thy choicest gifts in store
on her be pleased to pour,
long may she reign;
may she defend our laws,
and ever give us cause
to sing with heart and voice
God save the Queen!

195 God whose Son was once a man

Words: Peter Horrobin
Music: Greg Leavers

1 God whose Son was once a man on earth gave His life that
2 God whose power fell on the ear-ly Church, sent to earth from
3 Pour Your Spi-rit on the Church to-day, that Your life through

men may live. Ris-en, our as-cend-ed Lord ful-
heaven a-bove; Spi-rit led, by Him or-dained, they
me may flow; Spi-rit filled, I'll serve Your name and

-filled His pro-mised word. *When the Spi-rit came, the*
showed the world God's love.
live the truth I know. (after v. 3) *When the Spi-rit comes, new*

Church was born, God's peo-ple shared in a bright new dawn. *They*
life is born, God's peo-ple share in a bright new dawn. *We'll*

196 Good Christian men, rejoice

IN DULCI JUBILO   Irregular

Words: John Mason Neale (1818–66)
Music: German Carol melody, 14th cent.

Good Christ - ian men,___ re - joice_____ with

heart and soul___ and voice!_____ Give ye heed to

what we say: News! News!   Je - sus Christ is

born to - day.   Ox and ass be - fore Him bow, and

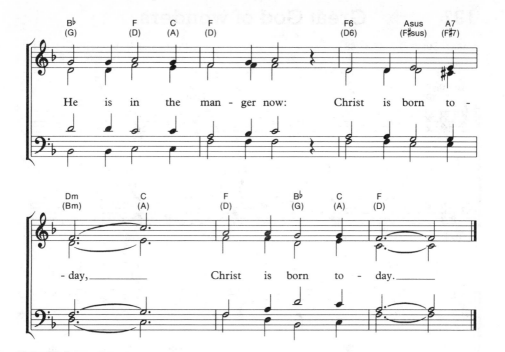

He is in the man - ger now: Christ is born to - day, Christ is born to - day.

1 Good Christian men, rejoice
with heart and soul and voice!
Give ye heed to what we say:
News! News! Jesus Christ is born today.
Ox and ass before Him bow,
and He is in the manger now:
Christ is born today,
Christ is born today.

2 Good Christian men, rejoice
with heart and soul and voice!
Now ye hear of endless bliss:
Joy! Joy! Jesus Christ was born for this.
He hath ope'd the heavenly door,
and man is blest for evermore:
Christ was born for this,
Christ was born for this.

3 Good Christian men, rejoice
with heart and soul and voice!
Now ye need not fear the grave:
Peace! Peace! Jesus Christ was born to save;
calls you one, and calls you all,
to gain His everlasting hall:
Christ was born to save,
Christ was born to save.

197 Great God of wonders

Carey (Surrey)   88 88 88

Words: Samuel Davies (1723–61) altd.
Music: H Carey (1692–1743)

Great God_ of won-ders, all_ Thy ways are match-less, god-like and_ di-vine; but the_ fair glo-ries of_ Thy grace more god-like and_ un-ri-valled shine: *Who is_ a_ pardon-ing_ God_ like_*

Thee? Or who_____ has grace so rich___ and free?

1 Great God of wonders, all Thy ways
   are matchless, godlike and divine;
   but the fair glories of Thy grace
   more godlike and unrivalled shine:
       Who is a pardoning God like Thee?
       Or who has grace so rich and free?

2 Such dire offences to forgive,
   such guilty daring souls to spare;
   this is Thy grand prerogative,
   and none shall in the honour share:
       Who is a pardoning God . . .

3 In wonder lost, with trembling joy,
   we take the pardon of our God,
   pardon for sins of deepest dye,
   a pardon sealed with Jesus' blood:
       Who is a pardoning God . . .

4 O may this glorious matchless love,
   this God-like miracle of grace,
   teach mortal tongues, like those above,
   to raise this song of lofty praise:
       Who is a pardoning God . . .

198 Gracious Spirit

CHARITY   777 5

Words: Christopher Wordsworth (1807–85)
Music: John Stainer (1840–1901)

Gra - cious Spi - rit, Ho - ly Ghost, taught by You, we co - vet most, of Your gifts at Pen - te - cost, ho - ly, heaven - ly love.

1 Gracious Spirit, Holy Ghost,
  taught by You, we covet most,
  of Your gifts at Pentecost,
  holy, heavenly love.

2 Faith that mountains could remove,
  tongues of earth or heaven above,
  knowledge, all things, empty prove
  without heavenly love.

3 Though I as a martyr bleed,
  give my goods the poor to feed,
  all is vain if love I need;
  therefore give me love.

4 Love is kind, and suffers long;
  love is meek, and thinks no wrong;
  love, than death itself more strong:
  therefore give us love.

5 Prophecy will fade away,
  melting in the light of day;
  love will ever with us stay:
  therefore give us love.

6 Faith, and hope, and love we see
  joining hand in hand, agree;
  but the greatest of the three,
  and the best, is love.

199 Great is the Lord

Words and music: Steve McEwan

Worshipfully

Great_____ is the Lord_ and most wor-thy of

praise, the ci-ty of our God, the ho-ly place, the

joy of the_ whole earth. _

Great_____ is the Lord in whom we have the vic - to-ry,_

Lord, we trust in Your un - fail - ing love, for
You a - lone are God e - ter - nal, Through-out earth and hea - ven a -
- bove._____

Great is the Lord and most worthy of praise,
the city of our God, the holy place,
the joy of the whole earth.
Great is the Lord in whom we have the victory,
He aids us against the enemy,
we bow down on our knees.

And Lord, we want to lift Your name on high,
and Lord, we want to thank You,
for the works You've done in our lives;
and Lord, we trust in Your unfailing love,
for You alone are God eternal,
throughout earth and heaven above.

200   Great is Thy faithfulness

GREAT IS THY FAITHFULNESS   11 10 11 10 with refrain

Words: T O Chisholm (1866–1960)
Music: W M Runyan (1870–1957)

Great is Thy faith - ful-ness, O God my Fa - ther,

there is no sha - dow of turn - ing with Thee;

Thou chang - est not, Thy com - pas - sions they fail not,

as Thou hast been Thou for - ev - er wilt be.

Great is Thy faith-ful-ness, great is Thy faith-ful-ness;

morn - ing by morn - ing new mer - cies I see;
all I have need - ed Thy hand hath pro - vid - ed, –
great is Thy faith - ful-ness, Lord, un - to me!

1 Great is Thy faithfulness, O God my Father,
   there is no shadow of turning with Thee;
   Thou changest not, Thy compassions they fail not,
   as Thou hast been Thou for ever wilt be.
       Great is Thy faithfulness,
       great is Thy faithfulness;
       morning by morning
       new mercies I see;
       all I have needed
       Thy hand hath provided, –
       great is Thy faithfulness, Lord, unto me!

2 Summer and winter, and spring-time and harvest,
   sun, moon and stars in their courses above,
   join with all nature in manifold witness
   to Thy great faithfulness, mercy and love.
       Great is Thy faithfulness . . .

3 Pardon for sin, and a peace that endureth,
   Thine own dear presence to cheer and to guide;
   strength for today and bright hope for tomorrow,
   blessings all mine, with ten thousand beside!
       Great is Thy faithfulness . . .

201 Guide me, O Thou great Jehovah

CWM RHONDDA   87 87 47 extended

Words: William Williams (1717–91) altd.
Music: John Hughes (1873–1932)

Guide me, O Thou great Je - ho - vah,
pil - grim through this bar - ren land; I am weak, but
Thou art __ migh - ty; hold me with Thy __ power - ful hand:
Bread of hea - ven, __ Bread of hea - ven, feed me now and ev - er -

- more,_____ feed me now_ and_ ev - er - more.

1 Guide me, O Thou great Jehovah,
  pilgrim through this barren land;
  I am weak, but Thou art mighty;
  hold me with Thy powerful hand:
      Bread of heaven,
  feed me now and evermore.

2 Open now the crystal fountain,
  whence the healing stream doth flow;
  let the fiery, cloudy pillar
  lead me all my journey through:
      Strong deliverer,
  be Thou still my strength and shield.

3 When I tread the verge of Jordan,
  bid my anxious fears subside:
  death of death, and hell's destruction,
  land me safe on Canaan's side:
      Songs of praises
  I will ever give to Thee.

202
Hail the day

LLANFAIR   77 77 with Alleluias

Words: Charles Wesley (1707–88)
and Thomas Cotterill (1779–1823)
Music: R Williams (1781–1821)

Hail the day that sees Him rise, Al - le - lu - ia,

to His throne be - yond the skies, Al - le - lu - ia,

Christ, the Lamb for sin - ners given, Al - le - lu - ia,___

en - ters now the high-est__ heaven: Al - le - lu - ia.

1 Hail the day that sees Him rise,
    Alleluia,
  to His throne beyond the skies;
  Christ, the Lamb for sinners given,
  enters now the highest heaven.

2 There for Him high triumph waits:
  lift your heads, eternal gates,
  He has conquered death and sin,
  take the King of glory in.

3 See! the heaven its Lord receives,
  yet He loves the earth He leaves;
  though returning to His throne,
  still He calls mankind His own.

4 Still for us He intercedes,
  His prevailing death He pleads,
  near Himself prepares our place,
  He the first-fruits of our race.

5 Lord, though parted from our sight,
  far beyond the starry height,
  lift our hearts that we may rise
  one with You beyond the skies.

6 There with You we shall remain,
  share the glory of Your reign,
  there Your face unclouded view,
  find our heaven of heavens in You.

203 Hail, Thou once despised Jesus

Lux Eoi   87 87 D

Words: John Bakewell (1721–1819)
Music: Arthur S Sullivan (1842–1900)

Hail, Thou once des - pi - sèd Je - sus, hail, Thou Ga - li - le - an King!

Thou didst suf - fer   to re - lease us, Thou didst free sal - va - tion bring.

Hail, Thou a - go - nis - ing Sav - iour, bear - er of our_ sin and shame;

by Thy mer - its   we find fa - vour;   life is giv - en through Thy name.

1 Hail, Thou once despisèd Jesus,
hail, Thou Galilean King!
Thou didst suffer to release us,
Thou didst free salvation bring.
Hail, Thou agonising Saviour,
bearer of our sin and shame;
by Thy merits we find favour;
life is given through Thy name.

2 Paschal Lamb, by God appointed,
all our sins on Thee were laid;
by almighty love anointed,
Thou hast full atonement made.
All Thy people are forgiven
through the virtue of Thy blood;
opened is the gate of heaven,
peace is made 'twixt man and God.

3 Jesus, hail! enthroned in glory,
there for ever to abide;
all the heavenly hosts adore Thee,
seated at Thy Father's side:
there for sinners Thou art pleading,
there Thou dost our place prepare;
ever for us interceding,
till in glory we appear.

4 Worship, honour, power, and blessing,
Thou art worthy to receive;
loudest praises, without ceasing,
meet it is for us to give:
Help, ye bright angelic spirits!
bring your sweetest, noblest lays;
help to sing our Saviour's merits,
help to chant Immanuel's praise.

204 Hail to the Lord's anointed

CRÜGER 76 76 D

Words: James Montgomery (1771–1854)
Music: adapted by W H Monk (1823–89)
from a chorale by J Crüger (1598–1662)

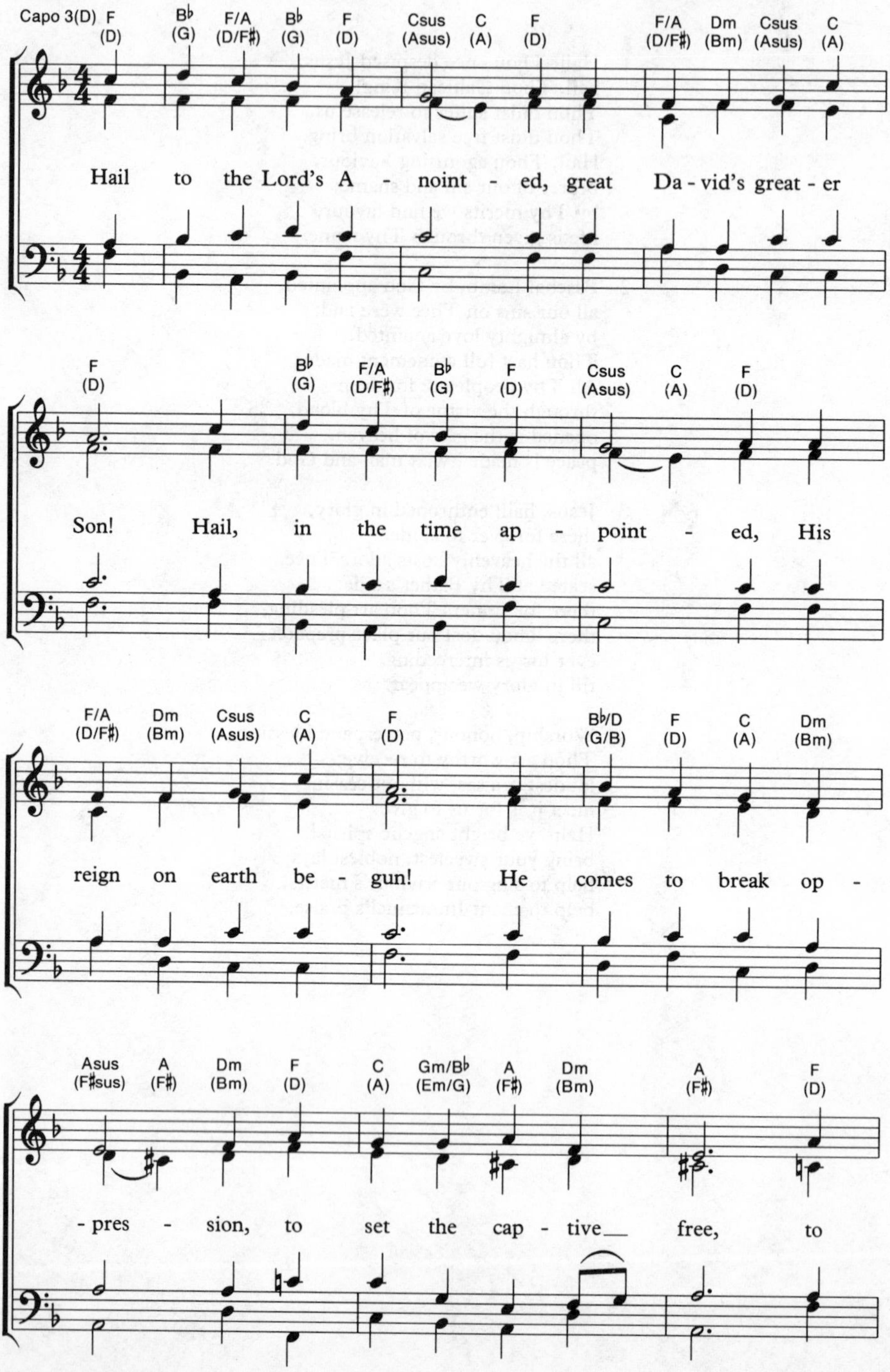

Capo 3(D)
F (D) B♭ (G) F/A (D/F♯) B♭ (G) F (D) Csus (Asus) C (A) F (D) F/A (D/F♯) Dm (Bm) Csus (Asus) C (A)
Hail to the Lord's A - noint - ed, great Da - vid's great - er
F (D) B♭ (G) F/A (D/F♯) B♭ (G) F (D) Csus (Asus) C (A) F (D)
Son! Hail, in the time ap - point - ed, His
F/A (D/F♯) Dm (Bm) Csus (Asus) C (A) F (D) B♭/D (G/B) F (D) C (A) Dm (Bm)
reign on earth be - gun! He comes to break op -
Asus (F♯sus) A (F♯) Dm (Bm) F (D) C (A) Gm/B♭ (Em/G) A (F♯) Dm (Bm) A (F♯) F (D)
- pres - sion, to set the cap - tive free, to

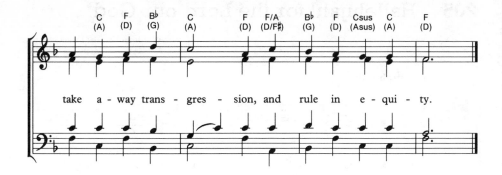

take a - way trans - gres - sion, and rule in e - qui - ty.

1   Hail to the Lord's anointed,
    great David's greater Son!
    Hail, in the time appointed,
    His reign on earth begun!
    He comes to break oppression,
    to set the captive free,
    to take away transgression,
    and rule in equity.

2   He comes with succour speedy
    to those who suffer wrong;
    to help the poor and needy,
    and bid the weak be strong;
    to give them songs for sighing,
    their darkness turn to light,
    whose souls, condemned and dying,
    were precious in His sight.

3   He shall come down like showers
    upon the fruitful earth;
    Love, joy, and hope, like flowers,
    spring in His path to birth:
    before Him, on the mountains,
    shall peace the herald go,
    and righteousness in fountains
    from hill to valley flow.

4   Kings shall fall down before Him,
    and gold and incense bring;
    all nations shall adore Him,
    His praise all people sing;
    to Him shall prayer unceasing
    and daily vows ascend;
    His kingdom still increasing,
    a kingdom without end.

5   O'er every foe victorious,
    He on His throne shall rest;
    from age to age more glorious,
    all-blessing and all-blest.
    The tide of time shall never
    His covenant remove;
    His name shall stand for ever,
    His changeless name of Love.

205 Hallelujah! for the Lord our God

Words and music: Dale Garratt

Triumphantly

Hal - le - lu - jah!_____ for the Lord our God the Al - migh - ty_____ reigns._____ Hal - le - lu - jah!_____ for the Lord our God the Al - migh - ty_____ reigns.

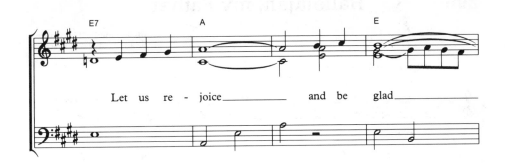

Let us re - joice_____ and be glad_____

_ and give the glo - ry un - to Him._____

_ Hal - le - lu - jah! for the Lord our

God the Al - migh - ty_____ reigns._____

Hallelujah, my Father

Words and music: Tim Cullen
Music arranged David Peacock

With quiet devotion

Hal - le - lu - jah, my Fa - ther, for giv - ing us Your Son; send - ing Him in to the world to be giv - en up for men, know - ing we would bruise Him and smite Him from the

earth. Hal-le-lu-jah, my_ Fa - ther, in His

death is my birth;___ Hal-le - lu - jah, my_

Fa - ther, in His life_ is my life.____

Hallelujah, my Father,
for giving us Your Son;
sending Him into the world
to be given up for men,
knowing we would bruise Him
and smite Him from the earth.
Hallelujah, my Father,
in His death is my birth;
Hallelujah, my Father,
in His life is my life.

207 Hallelujah! sing to Jesus

HALLELUJAH   87 87 D

Words: W C Dix (1837–98) altd.
Music: S S Wesley (1810–76)

1 Hallelujah! sing to Jesus,
　His the sceptre, His the throne;
　Hallelujah! His the triumph,
　His the victory alone.
　Hark! the songs of peaceful Zion
　thunder like a mighty flood;
　Jesus out of every nation
　hath redeemed us by His blood.

2 Hallelujah! not as orphans
　are we left in sorrow now;
　Hallelujah! He is near us,
　Faith believes, nor questions how.
　Though the cloud from sight received Him
　when the forty days were o'er,
　shall our hearts forget His promise,
　'I am with you evermore'?

3 Hallelujah! bread of heaven!
　Thou on earth our food, our stay;
　Hallelujah! here the sinful
　flee to Thee from day to day.
　Intercessor, friend of sinners,
　Earth's Redeemer, plead for me,
　where the songs of all the sinless
　sweep across the crystal sea.

4 Hallelujah! Hallelujah!
　Glory be to God on high;
　to the Father, and the Saviour,
　who has gained the victory;
　glory to the Holy Spirit,
　fount of love and sanctity.
　Hallelujah! Hallelujah!
　to the triune Majesty.

208 'Hallelujah', sing to the Lord

Words and music: Steve and Gina Southworth
Music arranged Christopher Norton

'Hal - le - lu - jah' sing to the Lord songs of praise; we bless You,_ Lord, we give to You glo - ry due_ Your ho - ly Name._ We stretch out our hands, we stretch out our hands un - to You, Lord. We lift up our

209 Hark, my soul

ST BEES 77 77

Words: William Cowper (1731–1800)
Music: John Bacchus Dykes (1823–76)

1 Hark, my soul! it is the Lord;
'Tis thy Saviour, hear His word;
Jesus speaks, and speaks to thee,
'Say, poor sinner, lov'st thou Me?'

2 'I delivered thee when bound,
and, when bleeding, healed thy wound;
sought thee wandering, set thee right,
turned thy darkness into light.'

3 Can a woman's tender care
cease towards the child she bare?
Yes, she may forgetful be,
yet will I remember Thee.

4 'Mine is an unchanging love,
higher than the heights above,
deeper than the depths beneath,
free and faithful, strong as death.'

5 'Thou shalt see My glory soon,
when the work of grace is done;
partner of My throne shalt be;
say, poor sinner, lov'st thou Me?'

6 Lord! it is my chief complaint
that my love is weak and faint;
yet I love Thee, and adore:
O for grace to love Thee more!

210   Hark, the glad sound

St Saviour   CM

Words: Philip Dodderidge (1702–51)
in this version Horrobin/Leavers
Music: F G Baker (1840–1908)

1   Hark, the glad sound! the Saviour comes,
     the Saviour promised long;
     let every heart prepare a throne,
     and every voice a song.

2   He comes, the prisoners to release
     in Satan's bondage held;
     the chains of sin before Him break,
     the iron fetters yield.

3   He comes to free the captive mind
     where evil thoughts control;
     and for the darkness of the blind,
     gives light that makes them whole.

4   He comes the broken heart to bind,
     the wounded soul to cure;
     and with the treasures of His grace
     to enrich the humble poor.

5   Our glad hosannas, Prince of Peace,
     Your welcome shall proclaim;
     and heaven's eternal arches ring
     with Your belovèd name.

211   Hark! the herald-angels sing

MENDELSSOHN   77 77 D with refrain

Words: Charles Wesley (1707–88) and others
Music: F Mendelssohn-Bartholdy (1809–47)
arranged W H Cummings (1831–1915)

Hark! the her - ald - an - gels sing__ 'Glo-ry to the new-born King!

Peace on earth, and mer - cy mild,__ God and sin - ners re - con-ciled.'

Joy-ful, all you na-tions rise,__ join the tri-umph of the skies;__

with th'an-gel - ic host pro - claim,__ 'Christ is__ born in Beth-le-hem!'

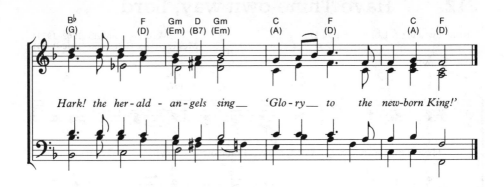

Hark! the her-ald - an-gels sing__ 'Glo-ry__ to the new-born King!'

1   Hark! the herald-angels sing
    'Glory to the new-born King!
    Peace on earth, and mercy mild,
    God and sinners reconciled.'
    Joyful, all you nations rise,
    join the triumph of the skies;
    with the angelic host proclaim,
    'Christ is born in Bethlehem!'
        Hark! the herald-angels sing
        'Glory to the new-born King!'

2   Christ by highest heaven adored,
    Christ, the everlasting Lord,
    late in time behold Him come,
    offspring of a virgin's womb!
    Veiled in flesh the Godhead see!
    Hail, the incarnate Deity!
    Pleased as man with man to dwell,
    Jesus, our Immanuel.
        Hark! the herald-angels sing
        'Glory to the new-born King!'

3   Hail, the heaven-born Prince of Peace!
    Hail, the Sun of righteousness!
    Light and life to all He brings,
    risen with healing in His wings.
    Mild He lays His glory by,
    born that man no more may die;
    born to raise the sons of earth,
    born to give them second birth.
        Hark! the herald-angels sing
        'Glory to the new-born King!'

212 Have Thine own way, Lord

THINE OWN WAY, LORD   54 54 D

Words: A A Pollard (1862–1934)
Music: George C Stebbins (1846–1945)

Have Thine own way, Lord, have Thine own way;___ Thou art the

pot - ter, I am the clay;___ mould me and make me af - ter Thy

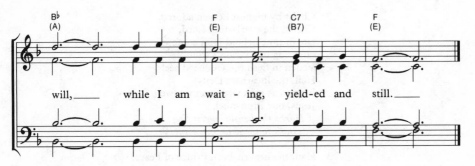

will,___ while I am wait - ing, yield-ed and still.___

1 Have Thine own way, Lord,
    have Thine own way;
Thou art the potter, I am the clay;
mould me and make me after Thy will,
while I am waiting, yielded and still.

2 Have Thine own way, Lord,
    have Thine own way;
search me and try me, Master, today.
Whiter than snow, Lord, wash me just now,
as in Thy presence humbly I bow.

3 Have Thine own way, Lord,
    have Thine own way;
wounded and weary, help me, I pray.
Power, all power, surely is Thine;
touch me and heal me, Saviour divine.

4 Have Thine own way, Lord,
    have Thine own way;
hold o'er my being absolute sway;
fill with Thy Spirit till all shall see
Christ only, always, living in me.

213   He gave me beauty

Words and music: Robert Whitney Manzano
Music arranged Christopher Norton

Lightly

He gave me beau-ty for ash-es, ___ the oil of joy for

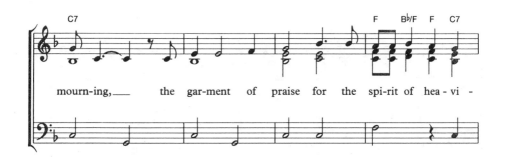

mourn-ing, ___ the gar-ment of praise for the spi-rit of hea-vi -

- ness; that we might be trees of right-eous-ness, the plant-ing of the

Lord, that He might be glo - ri - fied. _____

214   He gave His life

SELFLESS LOVE   86 86 D

Words: Christopher Porteous
Music: Andrew Maries

Unison

He gave His life in self-less love, for sin-ful man He came;

He had no stain of sin Him-self but bore our guilt and shame:

He took the cup of pain and death, His blood was free-ly shed;

we see His bo-dy on the cross, we share the liv-ing bread.

1 He gave His life in selfless love,
  for sinful man He came;
  He had no stain of sin Himself
  but bore our guilt and shame:
  He took the cup of pain and death,
  His blood was freely shed;
  we see His body on the cross,
  we share the living bread.

2 He did not come to call the good
  but sinners to repent;
  it was the lame, the deaf, the blind
  for whom His life was spent:
  to heal the sick, to find the lost –
  it was for such He came,
  and round His table all may come
  to praise His holy name.

3 They heard Him call His Father's name –
  then 'Finished!' was His cry;
  like them we have forsaken Him
  and left Him there to die:
  the sins that crucified Him then
  are sins His blood has cured;
  the love that bound Him to a cross
  our freedom has ensured.

4 His body broken once for us
  is glorious now above;
  the cup of blessing we receive,
  a sharing of His love:
  as in His presence we partake,
  His dying we proclaim
  until the hour of majesty
  when Jesus comes again.

215 He has showed you

Words and music: Graham Kendrick
Music arranged Christopher Norton

He has showed you, O man, what is good — and

what does the Lord re-quire of you? He has showed you, O man, what is

good — and what does the Lord re-quire of you, but to

act just-ly, and to love mer-cy, and to walk hum-bly with your

God;   but to   act just-ly, and to   love mer-cy, and to

walk hum - bly__ with   your   God.

He has

He has showed you, O man, what is good –
and what does the Lord require of you?
He has showed you, O man, what is good –
and what does the Lord require of you,
but to act justly, and to love mercy,
and to walk humbly with your God;
but to act justly, and to love mercy,
and to walk humbly with your God.
He has showed . . .

216 He is born, our Lord and Saviour

Words and music: Jimmy Owens

He is born, our Lord_ and Sav - iour:

He is born, our heaven - ly King: give Him hon - our,

give_ Him glo - ry, earth re - joice and hea - ven sing!

Born to be our sanc - tu - ar - y,_

born to bring us light and peace;
for our sins to bring forgiveness,
from our guilt to bring release.

1 He is born, our Lord and Saviour:
 He is born, our heavenly King:
 give Him honour, give Him glory,
 earth rejoice and heaven sing!
 Born to be our sanctuary,
 born to bring us light and peace;
 for our sins to bring forgiveness,
 from our guilt to bring release.

2 He who is from everlasting
 now becomes the incarnate Word;
 He whose name endures for ever
 now is born the Son of God:
 born to bear our griefs and sorrows,
 born to banish hate and strife;
 born to bear the sin of many,
 born to give eternal life!

3 Hail, the Holy One of Israel,
 chosen heir to David's throne;
 hail the brightness of His rising –
 to His light the gentiles come:
 plunderer of Satan's kingdom,
 downfall of his evil power;
 rescuer of all His people,
 conqueror in death's dark hour!

4 He shall rule with righteous judgement,
 and His godly rule extend;
 governor among the nations,
 His great kingdom has no end:
 He shall reign, the King of glory,
 higher than the kings of earth –
 Alleluia, alleluia!
 Praise we now His holy birth!

217

He is exalted

Words and music: Twila Paris

He is ex-alt-ed, the King is ex-alt-ed on__ high; I will praise__ Him. He is ex-alt-ed, for ev-er ex-alt-ed and I will praise His name!__ He is the Lord; for ev-er His truth shall

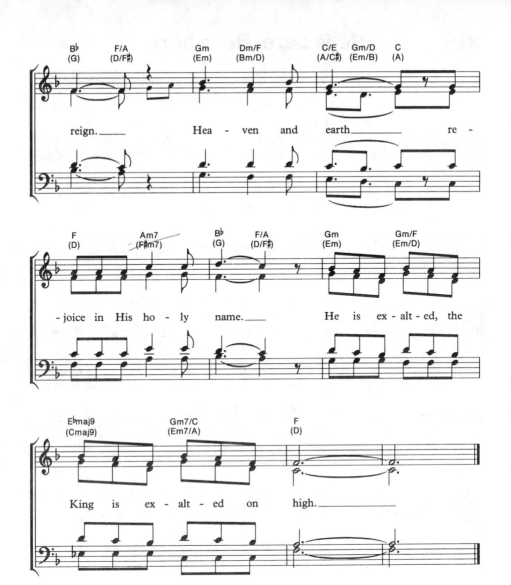

He is exalted,
the King is exalted on high;
I will praise Him.
He is exalted,
for ever exalted
and I will praise His name!

He is the Lord;
for ever His truth shall reign.
Heaven and earth
rejoice in His holy name.
He is exalted,
the King is exalted on high.

218 He is here, He is here

Words and music: Jimmy Owens
Music arranged Roland Fudge

1 He is here, He is here, He is moving a-
2 He is Lord, He is Lord, let us worship be-

-mong us; He is here, He is here, as we gather in His
-fore Him; He is Lord, He is Lord, as we gather in His

name!____ He is here, He is here, and He
name!____ He is Lord, He is Lord, let us

wants to work a won-der; He is here as we gather in His

Words and music: © 1972 Lexicon Music Inc (USA)/M P I Ltd

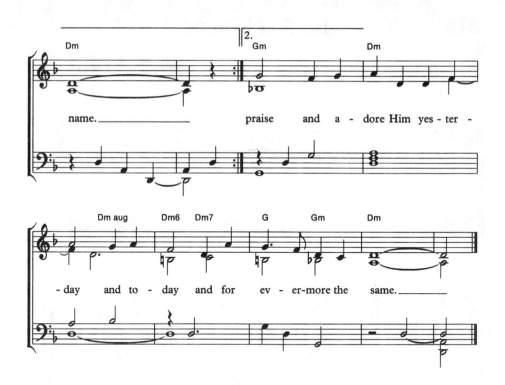

name._____ praise and a - dore Him yes - ter -

- day and to - day and for ev - er-more the same._____

1 He is here, He is here,
   He is moving among us;
   He is here, He is here,
   as we gather in His name!
   He is here, He is here,
   and He wants to work a wonder;
   He is here as we gather in His name.

2 He is Lord, He is Lord,
   let us worship before Him;
   He is Lord, He is Lord,
   as we gather in His name!
   He is Lord, He is Lord,
   let us praise and adore Him
   yesterday and today and for evermore the same.

219
He that is in us

Words and music: Graham Kendrick
Music arranged Christopher Norton

Lively

He that is in us is great-er than he that is in the world;

He that is in us is great-er than he that is in_____ the world.

There-fore I will sing and I will re-joice, for His

Spi - rit lives in me. Christ the liv-ing One has

o - ver - come, and we share in His vic - to - ry.

He that is in us is greater
than he that is in the world;
He that is in us is greater
than he that is in the world.

1   Therefore I will sing and I will rejoice,
    for His Spirit lives in me.
    Christ the living One has overcome,
    and we share in His victory.
        He that is in us . . .

2   All the powers of death and hell and sin
    lie crushed beneath His feet.
    Jesus owns the name above all names,
    crowned with honour and majesty.
        He that is in us . . .

    (Repeat verse 2, slowly and majestically)

220   He is Lord, He is Lord

Words and music: Marvin Frey
Music arranged Roland Fudge

He is Lord, He is Lord, He is ris-en from the dead and He is Lord! Ev-ery knee shall bow, ev-ery tongue con-fess that Je-sus Christ is Lord.

221 He walked where I walk

Words and music: Graham Kendrick
Music arranged Christopher Norton

1 He walked where I walk, He walked where I walk,
2 One of a ha-ted race, one of a ha-ted race,

He stood where I stand, He stood where I stand,
stung by the pre-ju-dice, stung by the pre-ju-dice,

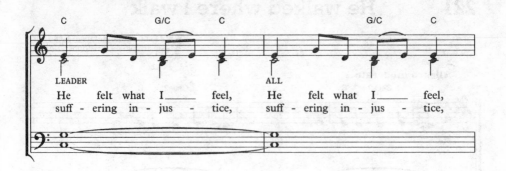

LEADER
He felt what I____ feel,
suff - ering in - jus - tice,

ALL
He felt what I____ feel,
suff - ering in - jus - tice,

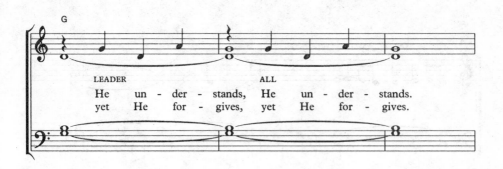

LEADER
He un - der - stands,
yet He for - gives,

ALL
He un - der - stands.
yet He for - gives.

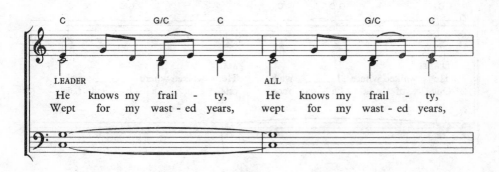

LEADER
He knows my frail - ty,
Wept for my wast - ed years,

ALL
He knows my frail - ty,
wept for my wast - ed years,

LEADER
shared my hu - ma - ni - ty,
paid for my wick - ed - ness,

ALL
shared my hu - ma - ni - ty,
paid for my wick - ed - ness,

222   He was pierced

Words and music: Maggi Dawn
Music arranged Christopher Norton

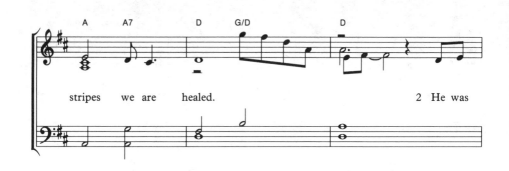

stripes   we are   healed.   2 He was

led   like   a lamb___   to   the   slaugh-ter,_____

___   al - though   He   was   in - no-cent   of   crime;

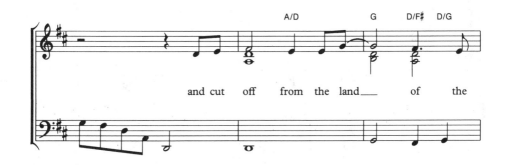

and   cut   off   from   the   land___   of   the

1 He was pierced for our transgressions,
and bruised for our iniquities;
and to bring us peace He was punished,
and by His stripes we are healed.

2 He was led like a lamb to the slaughter,
although He was innocent of crime;
and cut off from the land of the living,
He paid for the guilt that was mine.

We like sheep have gone astray,
turned each one to his own way,
and the Lord has laid on Him
the iniquity of us all.
We like sheep . . .

223 He who dwells

Words and music: Chris Bowater

_____ and I'll say of the Lord He is __ my strength. _____

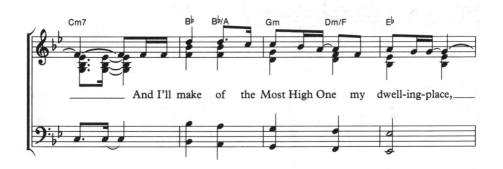

_____ And I'll make of the Most High One my dwell-ing-place, _____

_____ and I'll say He is __ my God, _____ I'll say He is __ my

God, __ I will say He is my God in whom I trust. _____

224   He who would valiant be

MONKS GATE   65 65 66 65

Words: after John Bunyan (1628–88)
Percy Dearmer (1867–1936)
Music: English traditional melody
arranged R Vaughan Williams (1872–1958)

He___ who would val - iant be 'gainst all dis - as - ter,___ let___ him in con - stan - cy fol - low the Mas - ter.___ There's___ no dis - cour - age - ment___ shall make him once re -

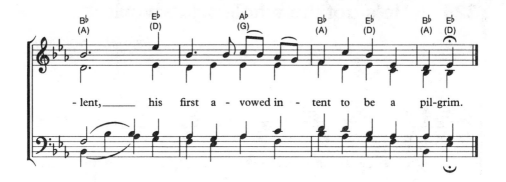

-lent,_____ his first a-vowed in-tent to be a pil-grim.

1 He who would valiant be
    'gainst all disaster,
    let him in constancy
    follow the Master.
    There's no discouragement
    shall make him once relent,
    his first avowed intent
    to be a pilgrim.

2 Who so beset him round
    with dismal stories,
    so but themselves confound –
    his strength the more is.
    No foes shall stay his might,
    though he with giants fight:
    he will make good his right
    to be a pilgrim.

3 Since, Lord, Thou dost defend
    us with Thy Spirit,
    we know we at the end
    shall life inherit.
    Then fancies flee away!
    I'll fear not what men say,
    I'll labour night and day
    to be a pilgrim.

225   He's got the whole wide world

Words and music: Unknown
Music arranged Phil Burt

He's got the whole wide world_____ in His hands, He's got the

whole wide world_____ in His hands, He's got the

whole wide world_____ in His hands, He's got the

whole world in His hands. He's got___ hands.

1   He's got the whole wide world in His hands,
    He's got the whole wide world in His hands,
    He's got the whole wide world in His hands,
    He's got the whole world in His hands.

2   He's got everybody here, in His hands, . . .

3   He's got the tiny little baby, in His hands . . .

4   He's got you and me brother, in His hands . . .

226   Healing God, almighty Father

HYFRYDOL   87 87 D

Words: John Richards
Music: R H Prichard (1811–87)

Heal - ing God,— al - migh - ty Fa - ther,
ac - tive— through - out— his - to - ry; ev - er
sav - ing, guid - ing, work - ing for— Your
child - ren— to— be free. Shep - herd, King,— in -

1 Healing God, almighty Father,
   active throughout history;
   ever saving, guiding, working
   for Your children to be free.
   Shepherd, King, inspiring prophets
   to foresee Your suffering role –
   Lord, we raise our prayers and voices;
   make us one and make us whole.

2 Healing Christ, God's Word incarnate,
   reconciling man to man;
   God's atonement, dying for us
   in His great redemptive plan.
   'Jesus', Saviour, Healer, Victor,
   drawing out for us death's sting;
   Lord, we bow our hearts in worship,
   and united praises bring.

3 Healing Spirit, Christ-anointing,
   raising to new life in Him;
   help the poor; release to captives;
   cure of body; health within.
   Life-renewing and empowering
   Christ-like service to the lost;
   Lord, we pray 'Renew Your wonders
   as of a New Pentecost!'

4 Healing Church, called-out and chosen
   to enlarge God's kingdom here;
   Lord-obeying; Spirit-strengthened
   to bring God's salvation near:
   for creation's reconciling
   gifts of love in us release.
   Father, Son and Holy Spirit
   'Make us instruments of peace.'

227 Hear my cry, O God

Words and music: Andy Silver

Hear my cry, O God, lis-ten to my prayer; from the ends of the earth will I call to You.

Hear my cry, O God, when my heart is o-ver-whelmed; lead me to the Rock that is high-er than I.

Teach me to trust in You,____ to pour out my heart to You;

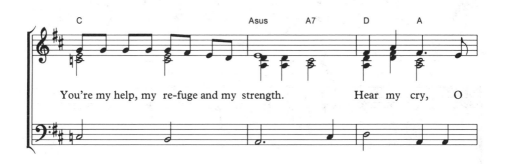

You're my help, my re-fuge and my strength. Hear my cry, O

God, lis - ten to my prayer; from the

ends of the earth will I call to You; hear my cry, O God.

228   Here from the world we turn

TRYST   64 64 66 64

Words: Frances van Alstyne (1820–1915)
(Fanny J Crosby)
Music: William H Doane (1832–1915)

1 Here from the world we turn, Jesus to seek;
   here may His loving grace graciously speak!
   Jesus, our dearest friend, while at Thy feet we bend,
   oh, let Thy smile descend! 'tis Thee we seek.

2 Come, Holy Comforter, Presence divine,
   now in our longing hearts graciously shine!
   Oh, for Thy mighty power! Oh, for a blessed shower,
   filling this hallowed hour with joy divine.

3 Saviour, Thy work revive! Here may we see
   those who are dead in sin quickened by Thee!
   Come to our hearts tonight, make every burden light,
   cheer Thou our waiting sight; we long for Thee.

229

Here I am

Words and music: Chris Bowater

Here I am, whol-ly a-vail-a-ble — as for me, I will serve the Lord. The fields are white un-to har-vest_____ but oh, the lab-'rers are so

Here I am, wholly available –
as for me, I will serve the Lord.

1   The fields are white unto harvest
    but oh, the labourers are so few;
    so Lord I give myself to help the reaping,
    to gather precious souls unto You.
      Here I am . . .

2   The time is right in the nation
    for works of power and authority;
    God's looking for a people who are willing
    to be counted in His glorious victory.
      Here I am . . .

3   As salt are we ready to savour,
    in darkness are we ready to be light;
    God's seeking out a very special people
    to manifest His truth and His might.
      Here I am . . .

230

Here, O my Lord

TOULON 10 10 10 10

Words: Horatius Bonar (1808–89)
Music: Louis Bourgeois (1510–61)

Here, O my Lord, I see Thee face to face;
here would I touch and handle things unseen,
here grasp with firmer hand th'eternal grace,
and all my weariness upon Thee lean.

1 Here, O my Lord, I see Thee face to face;
  here would I touch and handle things unseen,
  here grasp with firmer hand th'eternal grace,
  and all my weariness upon Thee lean.

2 Here would I feed upon the bread of God,
  here drink with Thee the royal wine of heaven;
  here would I lay aside each earthly load,
  here taste afresh the calms of sin forgiven.

3 Too soon we rise, the symbols disappear;
  the feast, though not the love, as past and gone;
  the bread and wine remove, but Thou art here,
  nearer than ever, still my shield and sun.

4 I have no help but Thine; nor do I need
  another arm save Thine to lean upon;
  it is enough, my Lord, enough indeed;
  my strength is in Thy might, Thy might alone.

5 Mine is the sin, but Thine the righteousness;
  mine is the guilt, but Thine the cleansing blood;
  here is my robe, my refuge, and my peace –
  Thy blood, Thy righteousness, O Lord my God.

6 Feast after feast thus comes and passes by,
  yet passing, points to the glad feast above,
  giving sweet foretaste of the festal joy,
  the Lamb's great bridal feast of bliss and love.

231 Hévénu shalom

Words: Chorus Israeli traditional song
Verses Michael Baughen
Music: Israeli traditional melody

Brightly

Hé-vé-nu sha - lom a - lé-chem, Hé-vé-nu sha - lom a-

- lé-chem, Hé-vé-nu sha - lom a - lé-chem, Hé-vé-nu

repeat for verses   last time

sha - lom, sha - lom, sha - lom a - lé-chem. Hé-vé-nu sha - lom a - lé-chem,

Hévénu shalom aléchem,
Hévénu shalom aléchem,
Hévénu shalom aléchem,
Hévénu shalom,
shalom, shalom aléchem.

1 Because He died and is risen,
  because He died and is risen,
  because He died and is risen,
  we now have peace with God
      through Jesus Christ our Lord.
  Hévénu shalom . . .

2 His peace destroys walls between us,
  His peace destroys walls between us,
  His peace destroys walls between us,
  for only He can reconcile
      us both to God.
  Hévénu shalom . . .

3 My peace I give you, said Jesus,
  My peace I give you, said Jesus,
  My peace I give you, said Jesus,
  don't let your heart be troubled,
      do not be afraid.
  Hévénu shalom . . .

4 The peace beyond understanding,
  the peace beyond understanding,
  the peace beyond understanding,
  will guard the hearts and minds
      of those who pray to Him.
  Hévénu shalom . . .

232 His hands were pierced

Words and music: D Woods

His hands were pierced, the hands that made the moun-tain range_ and ev - er - glade; that washed the stains of sin__ a - way_ and changed earth's dark - ness in - to day.

1 His hands were pierced, the hands that made
   the mountain range and everglade;
   that washed the stains of sin away
   and changed earth's darkness into day.

2 His feet were pierced, the feet that trod
   the furthest shining star of God;
   and left their imprint deep and clear
   on every winding pathway here.

3 His heart was pierced, the heart that burned
   to comfort every heart that yearned;
   and from it came a cleansing flood,
   the river of redeeming blood.

4 His hands and feet and heart, all three
   were pierced for me on Calvary;
   and here and now, to Him I bring
   my hands, feet, heart, an offering.

233 His name is higher

Words and music: Unknown
Music arranged Roger Mayor

1 His name is high-er_____ than a-ny oth-er,_____ His name is Je-sus,_____ His name is Lord. His name is Won-der-ful,_____ His name is Coun-sel-lor, His name is Prince of Peace,_____ the migh-ty God. His name is high-er_____ than a-ny oth-er,_____ His name is Je-sus, His name is Lord._____

234

His name is wonderful

Words and music: Audrey Mieir
Music arranged Norman Warren

His name is won-der-ful, His name is won-der-ful,
He is the migh-ty king, Mas-ter of ev-ery-thing,

His name is won-der-ful, Je-sus my Lord.

Je-sus my Lord. He's the great Shep-herd, the rock of all a-ges,

al-migh-ty God is He;_____ bow down be-fore Him,

love and a-dore Him, His name is won-der-ful, Je-sus my Lord!

Hold me Lord

Words and music: Danny Daniels
Music arranged Christopher Norton

Gently, but rhythmically

WOMEN Hold me Lord, in Your arms,

MEN Hold me Lord, in Your arms,

fill me Lord with Your Spi - rit; touch my heart

fill me Lord with Your Spi - rit; touch my heart

with Your love, let my life glo - ri - fy Your

with Your love, let my life glo - ri - fy Your

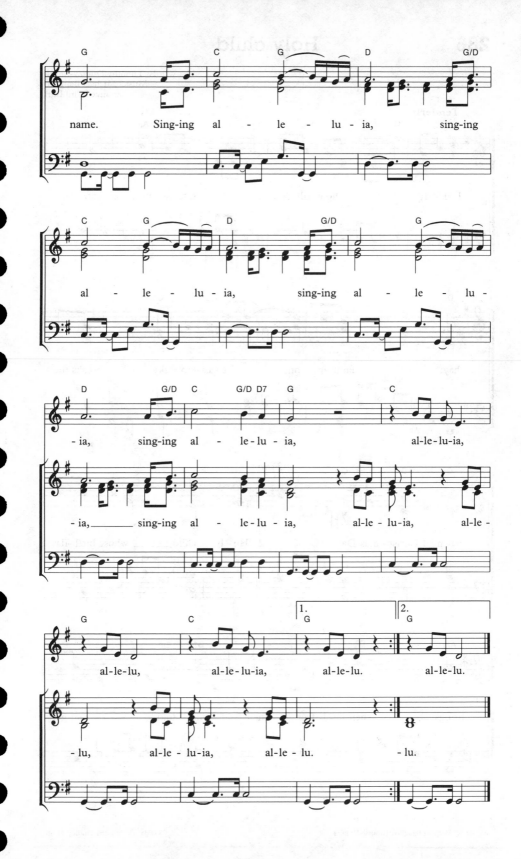

236   Holy child

Words: Timothy Dudley-Smith
Music: Michael Baughen
arranged Phil Burt

Tenderly

1 Ho-ly child,___ how still You lie! safe the man-ger, soft the hay; faint up - on___ the east-ern sky breaks the dawn of Christ - mas Day. 2 Ho - ly child,___ whose birth-day brings shep-herds from their field and fold, an-gel

choirs and east-ern kings, myrrh and frank - in-cense and gold:

1 Holy child, how still You lie!
safe the manger, soft the hay;
faint upon the eastern sky
breaks the dawn of Christmas Day.

2 Holy child, whose birthday brings
shepherds from their field and fold,
angel choirs and eastern kings,
myrrh and frankincense and gold:

3 Holy child, what gift of grace
from the Father freely willed!
In Your infant form we trace
all God's promises fulfilled.

4 Holy child, whose human years
span like ours delight and pain;
one in human joys and tears,
one in all but sin and stain:

5 Holy cnild, so far from home,
all the lost to seek and save:
to what dreadful death You come,
to what dark and silent grave!

6 Holy child, before whose name
powers of darkness faint and fall;
conquered death and sin and shame –
Jesus Christ is Lord of all!

7 Holy child, how still You lie!
safe the manger, soft the hay;
clear upon the eastern sky
breaks the dawn of Christmas Day.

237 Holy, holy, holy

NICAEA   11 12 12 10

Words: Reginald Heber (1783–1826)
Music: J B Dykes (1823–76)

Ho - ly, ho - ly, ho - ly,— Lord— God al - migh - ty!

ear - ly in the morn - ing our song shall rise to Thee;—

Ho - ly, ho - ly, ho - ly! — mer - ci - ful and migh - ty,

God— in three Per - sons,— bless - èd Tri - ni - ty!

1 Holy, holy, holy, Lord God almighty!
early in the morning our song shall rise to Thee;
Holy, holy, holy! – merciful and mighty,
God in three Persons, blessèd Trinity!

2 Holy, holy, holy! All the saints adore Thee,
casting down their golden crowns around the glassy sea;
cherubim and seraphim falling down before Thee,
who wast, and art, and evermore shall be.

3 Holy, holy, holy! – though the darkness hide Thee,
though the eye of sinful man Thy glory may not see;
only Thou art holy, there is none beside Thee,
perfect in power, in love, and purity.

4 Holy, holy, holy, Lord God almighty!
all Thy works shall praise Thy name, in earth, and sky, and sea:
Holy, holy, holy! – merciful and mighty,
God in three Persons, blessèd Trinity!

238 Holy, holy

Words and music: Jimmy Owens

Ho-ly, ho-ly, ho-ly, ho-ly, ho-ly, ho-ly,____ Lord God al-migh-ty! And we lift our hearts be-fore_ You as a to-ken of our love: ho-ly, ho-ly, ho-ly, ho-ly. Grac-ious -lu-jah.

1 Holy, holy, holy, holy,
  holy, holy, Lord God almighty!
  And we lift our hearts before You
  as a token of our love:
  holy, holy, holy, holy.

2 Gracious Father, gracious Father,
  we're so glad to be Your children, gracious Father;
  as we lift our heads before You
  as a token of our love,
  gracious Father, gracious Father.

3 Precious Jesus, precious Jesus,
  we're so glad that You've redeemed us, precious Jesus;
  and we lift our hands before You
  as a token of our love,
  precious Jesus, precious Jesus.

4 Holy Spirit, Holy Spirit,
  come and fill our hearts anew, Holy Spirit! –
  and we lift our voice before You
  as a token of our love,
  Holy Spirit, Holy Spirit.

5 Hallelujah, hallelujah,
  hallelujah, hallelujah –
  and we lift our hearts before You
  as a token of our love,
  hallelujah, hallelujah.

239   # Holy, holy, holy is the Lord

Words and music: Unknown
Music arrangement: Norman Warren

1 Holy, holy, holy is the Lord;
holy is the Lord God almighty!
Holy, holy, holy is the Lord;
holy is the Lord God almighty!
Who was, and is, and is to come!
Holy, holy, holy is the Lord!

2 Jesus, Jesus, Jesus is the Lord;
Jesus is the Lord God almighty!
Jesus, Jesus, Jesus is the Lord;
Jesus is the Lord God almighty!
Who was, and is, and is to come!
Jesus, Jesus, Jesus is the Lord!

3 Worthy, worthy worthy is the Lord;
worthy is the Lord God almighty!
Worthy, worthy worthy is the Lord;
worthy is the Lord God almighty!
Who was, and is, and is to come!
Worthy, worthy, worthy is the Lord!

4 Glory, glory, glory to the Lord;
glory to the Lord God almighty!
Glory, glory, glory to the Lord;
glory to the Lord God almighty!
Who was, and is, and is to come!
Glory, glory, glory to the Lord!

240 Holy is the Lord

Words and music: Kelly Green
Music arranged Christopher Norton

Majestically

MEN AND WOMEN IN CANON

MEN Ho - ly___ is___ the___ Lord.
WOMEN Ho - ly___ is___ the *etc.*

Ho - ly___ is___ the___ Lord.

Ho - ly___ is___ the___ Lord.

Ho - ly___ is___ the___ Lord.

Right-eous-ness_____ and mer - cy, Judge - ment_____ and

grace. Faith-ful - ness_____ and sov-ereign-ty;

Ho - ly is the Lord, Ho - ly is the

1.
Lord.

2.
Lord._____

241 Holy Spirit, we welcome You

Words and music: Chris Bowater

Lyrics:

Ho-ly Spi-rit,_ we wel-come You,_

Move a-mong us_ with ho-ly fire_ as we lay a-side_ all earth-ly de-sire,_

Words and music: © 1986 Lifestyle Ministries/
Word Music (UK), (a division of Word (UK) Ltd)
9 Holdom Avenue, Bletchley, Milton Keynes MK1 1QR, UK

2 Holy Spirit, we welcome You,
Holy Spirit, we welcome You!
Let the breeze of Your presence blow
that Your children here might truly know
how to move in the Spirit's flow.
Holy Spirit, Holy Spirit,
Holy Spirit, we welcome You!

3 Holy Spirit, we welcome You,
Holy Spirit, we welcome You!
Please accomplish in us today
some new work of loving grace, we pray –
unreservedly – have Your way.
Holy Spirit, Holy Spirit,
Holy Spirit, we welcome You!

242   Hosanna, hosanna

Words and music: Carl Tuttle

1 Ho - san - na, ho - san - na, ho - san - na in the high - est; ho - san - na, ho - san - na, ho - san - na in the high - est:

2 Glo - ry, glo - ry, glo - ry to the King of kings; glo - ry, glo - ry, glo - ry to the King of kings:

Lord, we lift up Your name, with hearts full of praise.

Be ex - alt - ed, O___ Lord my God– ho -

- san - na, in the high - est.
glo - ry to the King of kings.

1 Hosanna, hosanna, hosanna in the highest;
   hosanna, hosanna, hosanna in the highest:
   Lord, we lift up Your name,
   with hearts full of praise.
   Be exalted, O Lord my God –
   hosanna, in the highest.

2 Glory, glory, glory to the King of kings;
   glory, glory, glory to the King of kings:
   Lord, we lift up Your name
   with hearts full of praise.
   Be exalted, O Lord my God –
   glory to the King of kings.

243 How firm a foundation

MONTGOMERY   11 11 11 11

Words: 'K' in Rippon's *Selection*, 1787 altd.
Music: probably Samuel Jarvis (d 1785)

How firm a foun - da - tion, ye saints of the Lord,

is laid for your faith in His ex - cel - lent word;

what more can He say than to you He hath said,___

you___ who un - to Je - sus for re - fuge have fled?

1 How firm a foundation, ye saints of the Lord,
  is laid for your faith in His excellent word;
  what more can He say than to you He hath said,
  you who unto Jesus for refuge have fled?

2 Fear not, He is with thee, O be not dismayed;
  for He is thy God, and will still give thee aid:
  He'll strengthen thee, help thee, and cause thee to stand,
  upheld by His righteous, omnipotent hand.

3 In every condition, in sickness, in health,
  in poverty's vale, or abounding in wealth;
  at home and abroad, on the land, on the sea,
  as thy days may demand shall thy strength ever be.

4 When through the deep waters He calls thee to go,
  the rivers of grief shall not thee overflow;
  for He will be with thee in trouble to bless,
  and sanctify to thee thy deepest distress.

5 When through fiery trials thy pathway shall lie,
  His grace all-sufficient shall be thy supply;
  the flame shall not hurt thee, His only design
  thy dross to consume and thy gold to refine.

6 The soul that on Jesus has leaned for repose
  He will not, He will not, desert to its foes;
  that soul, though all hell should endeavour to shake,
  He'll never, no never, no never forsake.

244 How good is the God we adore

CELESTE LM

Words: Joseph Hart (1712–68)
Music: from *Lancashire Sunday School Songs*, 1857

1 How good is the God we adore!
   Our faithful, unchangeable friend:
   His love is as great as His power
   and knows neither measure nor end.

2 For Christ is the first and the last;
   His Spirit will guide us safe home:
   we'll praise Him for all that is past
   and trust Him for all that's to come.

245   How great is our God

Words and music: Unknown
Music arranged Phil Burt

With life

How great is our God,_____ how great is His name,_____

_ how great is His love_____ for - ev - er the same._____

_ He rolled back the wa - ters_____ of the migh-ty Red Sea,_____

_ and He said, 'I'll ne-ver leave you,_____ put your trust in Me.'_____

246 How I love You

Words and music: Keith Green

247 How lovely is Thy dwelling-place

Words: from Psalm 84
Music: Scottish traditional folk melody
arranged Jonathan Asprey

1 and 4 How love-ly is_____ Thy dwell-ing-place,
2 Ev-en the spar-row finds a home_
3 And I'd ra-ther be_____ a_____ door-keep-er____

— O_____ Lord of hosts, to_ me;_____ my_
where_ he can set-tle_ down;_____ and the
and____ on-ly stay_ a_ day,_____ than_

248 How lovely is Thy dwelling-place

Words: from Psalm 84
Music: Unknown
arranged Phil Burt

How love-ly is Thy dwell-ing-place, O Lord of hosts, my soul longs and yearns for Your courts,_____ and my heart and flesh sing for joy to the liv-ing God._____ One

249   How lovely on the mountains

Words and music: Leonard E Smith Jnr
Music arranged David Peacock

How love-ly on the moun-tains are the feet of Him who brings good news, good news, pro-claim-ing peace, an-nounc-ing news of hap-pi-ness, Our God reigns, our God reigns!

Our God reigns,_____ our God reigns,_____

our God reigns,_____ our God reigns!_____

POPULAR VERSION

1 How lovely on the mountains are the feet of Him
who brings good news, good news,
proclaiming peace, announcing news of happiness,
Our God reigns, our God reigns!
  Our God reigns, our God reigns! (*twice*)

2 You watchmen lift your voices joyfully as one,
shout for your King, your King.
See eye to eye the Lord restoring Zion:
your God reigns, your God reigns!

3 Waste places of Jerusalem break forth with joy,
We are redeemed, redeemed.
The Lord has saved and comforted His people:
your God reigns, your God reigns!

4 Ends of the earth, see the salvation of your God,
Jesus is Lord, is Lord.
Before the nations He has bared His holy arm:
your God reigns, your God reigns!

Original version of words overleaf

ORIGINAL VERSION

1 How lovely on the mountains are the feet of Him
who brings good news, good news,
proclaiming peace, announcing news of happiness,
Our God reigns, our God reigns!
   Our God reigns, our God reigns! (*twice*)

2 He had no stately form, He had no majesty,
that we should be drawn to Him.
He was despised and we took no account of Him,
yet now He reigns with the Most High.
   Now He reigns, now He reigns,
   now He reigns with the Most High!

3 It was our sin and guilt that bruised and wounded Him,
it was our sin that brought Him down.
When we like sheep had gone astray, our Shepherd came
and on His shoulders bore our shame.
   On His shoulders, on His shoulders,
   on His shoulders He bore our shame.

4 Meek as a lamb that's led out to the slaughterhouse,
dumb as a sheep before its shearer,
His life ran down upon the ground like pouring rain,
that we might be born again.
   That we might be, that we might be,
   that we might be born again.

5 Out from the tomb He came with grace and majesty,
He is alive, He is alive.
God loves us so – see here His hands, His feet, His side,
Yes, we know He is alive.
   He is alive, He is alive,
   He is alive, He is alive!

6 How lovely on the mountains are the feet of Him
who brings good news, good news,
announcing peace, proclaiming news of happiness:
our God reigns, our God reigns.
   Our God reigns, our God reigns,
   our God reigns, our God reigns!

250 How shall they hear

OMBERSLEY LM

Words: Timothy Dudley-Smith
Music: W H Gladstone (1840–91)

How shall they hear, who have not heard news of a
Lord who loved and came? nor known His re - con - cil - ing
word, nor learned to trust the Sav - iour's name?

1 How shall they hear, who have not heard
news of a Lord who loved and came?
nor known His reconciling word,
nor learned to trust the Saviour's name?

2 To all the world, to every place,
neighbours and friends and far-off lands,
preach the good news of saving grace;
go while the great commission stands.

3 'Whom shall I send?' who hears the call,
constant in prayer, through toil and pain,
telling of one who died for all,
to bring a lost world home again?

4 'Lord, here am I,' Your fire impart
to this poor cold self-centred soul;
touch but my lips, my hands, my heart,
and make a world for Christ my goal.

5 Spirit of love, within us move:
Spirit of truth, in power come down!
So shall they hear and find and prove
Christ is their life, their joy, their crown.

251   How sweet the name of Jesus

St Peter   CM

Words: John Newton (1725–1807) altd.
Music: A R Reinagle (1799–1877)

How sweet the name of Je - sus sounds in

a be - liev - er's ear! It___ soothes his sor - rows,

heals his wounds, and drives a - way his fear.

1   How sweet the name of Jesus sounds
    in a believer's ear!
    It soothes his sorrows, heals his wounds,
    and drives away his fear.

2   It makes the wounded spirit whole,
    and calms the troubled breast;
    'tis manna to the hungry soul,
    and to the weary rest.

3   Dear name! the rock on which I build,
    my shield and hiding-place,
    my never-failing treasury, filled
    with boundless stores of grace.

4   Jesus! my shepherd, brother, friend,
    my prophet, priest and king;
    my lord, my life, my way, my end,
    accept the praise I bring.

5   Weak is the effort of my heart,
    and cold my warmest thought;
    but when I see Thee as Thou art,
    I'll praise Thee as I ought.

6   Till then I would Thy love proclaim
    with every fleeting breath;
    and may the music of Thy name
    refresh my soul in death!

252   How precious, O Lord

Words and music: Phil Rogers
Music arranged Christopher Norton

How pre-cious, O Lord, is Your un-fail-ing

love; we find re-fuge in the sha-dow of Your

wings._____ We feast, Lord Je-sus,___ on the a-

-bun-dance of Your house and drink from Your

253 Hushed was the evening hymn

SAMUEL 66 66 88

Words: J D Burns (1823–64)
altered Horrobin/Leavers
Music: Arthur S Sullivan (1842–1900)

Hushed was the eve-ning hymn, the tem-ple courts were dark;___ the lamp was burn-ing dim be-fore the sa-cred ark, when sud-den-ly a voice di-vine rang through the sil-ence of the shrine.

1   Hushed was the evening hymn,
     the temple courts were dark;
     the lamp was burning dim
     before the sacred ark,
     when suddenly a voice divine
     rang through the silence of the shrine.

2   The old man, meek and mild,
     the priest of Israel, slept;
     his watch the temple child,
     the little Samuel, kept:
     and what from Eli's sense was sealed
     the Lord to Hannah's son revealed.

3   O give me Samuel's ear,
     the open ear, O Lord,
     alive and quick to hear
     each whisper of Your word –
     like him to answer at Your call,
     and to obey You first of all.

4   O give me Samuel's heart,
     a lowly heart, that waits
     to serve and play the part
     You show us at Your gates,
     by day and night, a heart that still
     moves at the breathing of Your will.

5   O give me Samuel's mind,
     a sweet, unmurmuring faith,
     obedient and resigned
     to You in life and death,
     that I may read with childlike eyes
     truths that are hidden from the wise.

254 I am a new creation

Words and music: Dave Bilbrough
Music arranged David Peacock

I am a new creation, no more in con-demnation, here in the grace of God I stand.

My heart is overflowing, my love just keeps on growing, here in the grace of God I stand. And I will praise

255   I am a wounded soldier

Words and music: Danny Daniels
Music arranged Christopher Norton

Gospel feel

Capo 3(D)

I am a wound-ed sol - dier_ but I will not leave the fight,___ be - cause the Great Phy-si - cian is heal - ing_ me.___ So I'm_ stand-ing in the bat - tle,_ in the

I am a wounded soldier
but I will not leave the fight,
because the Great Physician is healing me.

So I'm standing in the battle,
in the armour of His light,
because His mighty power is real in me.

I am loved, I am accepted
by the Saviour of my soul;
I am loved, I am accepted
and my wounds will be made whole.

256   I am not mine own

Words and music: Chris Bowater

I am not mine own, I've been bought with a price.

Pre - cious blood of Christ, I am not mine own.

1 I am not mine own,
   I've been bought with a price.
   Precious blood of Christ,
   I am not mine own.

2 I belong to You,
   I've been bought with a price.
   Precious blood of Christ,
   I belong to You.

3 How could I ever say
   'I will choose another way',
   knowing the price that's paid;
   precious blood of Christ.

257   I am not skilled

EWHURST   88 87

Words: Dora Greenwell (1821–82)
altered Horrobin/Leavers
Music: Cecil John Allen (1886–1973)

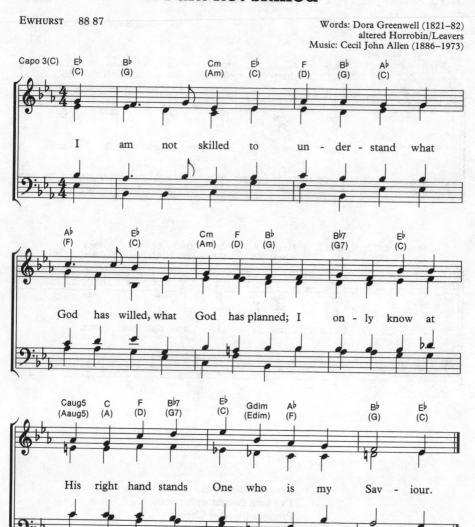

1 I am not skilled to understand
what God has willed, what God has planned;
I only know at His right hand
stands One who is my Saviour.

2 I take Him at His word indeed:
'Christ died for sinners,' this I read;
and in my heart I find a need
of Him to be my Saviour.

3 That He should leave His place on high
and come for sinful man to die,
you count it strange? so once did I,
before I knew my Saviour.

4 And O that He fulfilled may see
the glory of His life in me,
and with His work contented be,
as I with my dear Saviour.

5 Yea, living, dying, let me bring
my life, to Him an offering,
that He who lives to be my King
once died to be my Saviour.

258 I am trusting Thee

BULLINGER 85 83

Words: Frances Ridley Havergal (1836–79)
Music: E W Bullinger (1837–1913)

1 I am trusting Thee, Lord Jesus,
trusting only Thee;
trusting Thee for full salvation,
great and free.

2 I am trusting Thee for pardon,
at Thy feet I bow;
for Thy grace and tender mercy,
trusting now.

3 I am trusting Thee for cleansing
in the crimson flood;
trusting Thee to make me holy
by Thy blood.

4 I am trusting Thee to guide me;
Thou alone shalt lead,
every day and hour supplying
all my need.

5 I am trusting Thee for power,
Thine can never fail;
words which Thou Thyself shalt give me
must prevail.

6 I am trusting Thee, Lord Jesus;
never let me fall;
I am trusting Thee for ever,
and for all.

I am trusting in You

Words and music: Andy and Becky Silver

wait for You my hope will not be in vain.___

not be in vain.___ There may be prob -

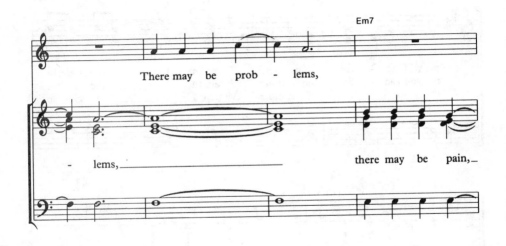

There may be prob - lems,

- lems,_____ there may be pain,___

there may be pain,___ but my hope will not be in vain.___

_____ but my hope will not be in vain.___

260

I am the Bread

Words and music: Brian Hoare

1 I am the Bread,_____ the Bread of Life;_____ who comes to
(2) Vine,_____ the liv-ing Vine;_____ a-part from
(3) bread,_____ and drink this wine,_____ and as you

me will ne-ver hun-ger. I am the Bread,_____ the Bread of
me you can do no-thing. I am the Vine,_____ the re-al
do, re-ceive this life of mine. All that I am_____ I give to

heaven;_____ who feeds on me will ne-ver die._____ *And as you*
Vine:_____ a-bide in me and I in you._____ *And as you*
you,_____ that you may live for ev-er- -more.

*eat,*_____ re-mem-ber *me* =_____ my bo-dy
*drink,*_____ re-mem-ber *me* =_____ my blood was

bro - ken on the tree:＿ my life was given＿ to set you
shed＿ up - on the tree:＿ my life was given＿ to set you

free,＿ and I'm a - live for ev - er - more. 2 I am the
free,＿ and I'm a - live for ev - er - more. 3 So eat this

1 I am the Bread,
   the Bread of Life;
   who comes to me will never hunger.
   I am the Bread,
   the Bread of heaven;
   who feeds on me will never die.
     And as you eat, remember me –
     my body broken on the tree:
     my life was given to set you free,
     and I'm alive for evermore.

2 I am the Vine,
   the living Vine;
   apart from me you can do nothing.
   I am the Vine,
   the real Vine:
   abide in me and I in you.
     And as you drink, remember me –
     my blood was shed upon the tree:
     my life was given to set you free,
     and I'm alive for evermore.

3 So eat this bread,
   and drink this wine,
   and as you do, receive this life of mine.
   All that I am I give to you,
   that you may live for evermore.

261 I am the Bread of Life

Words and music: S Suzanne Toolan
Music arranged Betty Pulkingham

Rich and full

Capo 3(G)

1 I am the Bread of Life; he who comes to Me shall not
(2) bread that I will give is My flesh for the life of the
(3) -less you eat of the flesh of the Son of
4 I am the Re - sur - rec - tion, I am the
(5) Lord, we be - lieve that You are the

hun - ger; he who believes in Me shall not thirst. No one can come to
world; and he who eats of this bread, he shall live for
Man and drink of His blood, and drink of His
Life; he who be - lieves in Me, ev - en if he
Christ, the Son of God, who has

Me un - less the Fa - ther draw him.
ev - er, he shall live for ev - er.
blood, you shall not have life with - in you. *And I will*
die, he shall live for ev - er.
come in - to the world.

Index of First Lines

Titles which differ from first lines are shown in italics
Numbers in brackets refer to the number of the item in Mission Praise 1 (1–282),
Mission Praise 2 (283–647), and Mission Praise Supplement (648–758).

Items 1 to 261 are in the Musicians' Edition volume 1,
items 262 to 536 in volume 2 and items 537 to 798 in volume 3.